TECHNOLOGY
AND INTERNATIONAL
RELATIONS

EDITED BY WILLIAM FIELDING OGBURN

TECHNOLOGY AND INTERNATIONAL RELATIONS

BERNARD BRODIE

WILLIAM T. R. FOX

HORNELL HART

ROBERT LEIGH

WILLIAM FIELDING OGBURN

ABBOTT PAYSON USHER

QUINCY WRIGHT

THE UNIVERSITY OF CHICAGO PRESS · CHICAGO

THE
NORMAN WAIT HARRIS MEMORIAL FOUNDATION

The Twenty-fourth Institute

QUINCY WRIGHT · *DIRECTOR*

THE Harris Foundation Lectures at the University of Chicago have been made possible through the generosity of the heirs of Norman Wait Harris and Emma Gale Harris, who donated to the University a fund to be known as "The Norman Wait Harris Memorial Foundation" on January 27, 1923. The letter of gift contains the following statement:

The purpose of the foundation shall be the promotion of a better understanding on the part of American citizens of the other peoples of the world, thus establishing a basis for improved international relations and a more enlightened world order. The aim shall always be to give accurate information, not to propagate opinion.

Annual Institutes have been held at the University of Chicago since the summer of 1924. The lectures delivered or the papers presented each year have been published in essentially their original form in a series of volumes of which this is the most recent.

THE UNIVERSITY OF CHICAGO PRESS, CHICAGO 37
Cambridge University Press, London, N.W. 1, England
W. J. Gage & Co., Limited, Toronto 2B, Canada

*Copyright 1949 by The University of Chicago. All rights reserved
Published 1949. Composed and printed by* THE UNIVERSITY OF
CHICAGO PRESS, *Chicago, Illinois, U.S.A.*

PREFACE

THE contents of this book are the outcome of the twenty-fourth annual Institute of the Norman Wait Harris Memorial Foundation held May 7, 8, and 9, 1948, at the Shoreland Hotel, Chicago, Illinois. The subject of the Institute was "Technology and International Relations." Several reasons existed for this choice of subject. One was the fact of an impressive constellation of inventions and scientific discoveries in transportation, in communication, and in mechanical power, many of which have a bearing on international relations. Also the period after a great war is an occasion for changes in the fundamental policies of one nation to another. Particularly the United States is re-examining the foundations of her own policies. It seemed, therefore, a good time to make some inquiries regarding these basic elements of policy as they may be affected by the new and revolutionary technological and scientific developments.

The remarkable collection of new inventions and scientific discoveries, which the postwar populations inherit and which make these years more notable than others, results from the part the war played in developing science and invention in certain lines. Ordinarily this decade would have been rich in invention anyway, but not so rich in these areas as it is because of the war. Though few of the new inventions originated during the war, they were matured and developed for use much faster because of the war. Atomic fission and the atomic bomb are good illustrations.

This list of new scientific developments comprises the various kinds of new airplanes—the helicopter, rockets, missiles, jet-propulsion engines, turbo-jet power plants—armored tanks, motored guns, bacteria bombs, poison gases, discoveries in nutrition, sanitation, surgery, and medicine, proximity fuses, high-octane fuels, fractionated motors, television, radar, the magnetic wire recorder, facsimile transmission, point-to-point radio telephones, photoprinting, photographic mapping, microfilm, artificial rubber, gasoline from coal, Diesel engines, plastics, plywood, magnesium, aluminum, and steel alloys.

Each of these inventions is in reality a cluster of several inventions around the central invention by which it is named. For instance, the airplane in the form in which it affects international relations includes explosives, telephones, high-octane fuels, fractionated motors, etc. From this list of clusters of inventions, which vary greatly in their significance for international relations, there are three which are unusually important. These are aviation, the atomic bomb, and the mass-communication inventions. In addition, there is the huge cluster around steam and steel that created what we call the Industrial Revolution, which, though not new to Britain, the United States, and Germany, is relatively new to the Soviet Union, is beginning in India, and will be new to China.

The Institute meetings centered around the implications of these four inventional complexes—steam and steel, the airplane, the atomic bomb, and the mass-communication inventions. However, discussion was not restricted to these four, and the program contained some general papers on technology, technological influences, and method.

The subject of this Institute was one in which there has not been much scientific research; and this fact should be remembered by the reader. For this reason the papers and discussions were less restricted and in a sense more interesting than they would have been if the papers had been confined merely to the presentation of facts or the results of scientific research. The field of technology and international relations is, furthermore, a broad one, and the Institute meetings were pioneering ventures. They should be thought of as exploring a relatively new field.

The approaches to the subject also varied among the contributors. Some dealt with broad fundamental relationships or were concerned with the basic elements of international relations or with outstanding influences of technology. Others chose to deal with very specific policies between the United States and other countries now or in the very near future on particular issues that are acute. Thus there are variations among the contributors between immediate and long-run policies and between the particular and the basic.

In view of these variations, it seemed desirable to write an introduction and there to present some fundamental relationships between inventions and the state to which all the chapters by the different authors can be related and classified. With such common themes set forth, the interconnection and unity of the following articles will be more apparent to the reader.

WILLIAM FIELDING OGBURN

UNIVERSITY OF CHICAGO
January 1949

TABLE OF CONTENTS

INTRODUCTORY IDEAS ON INVENTIONS AND THE STATE 1
   William Fielding Ogburn

THE PROCESS OF ADJUSTMENT TO NEW INVENTIONS 16
   William Fielding Ogburn

TECHNOLOGY AND THE GROWTH OF POLITICAL AREAS 28
   Hornell Hart

THE STEAM AND STEEL COMPLEX AND INTERNATIONAL RELATIONS . . . 58
   Abbott Payson Usher

AVIATION AND INTERNATIONAL RELATIONS 86
   William Fielding Ogburn

ATOMIC ENERGY AND INTERNATIONAL RELATIONS 102
   William T. R. Fox

THE MASS-COMMUNICATIONS INVENTIONS AND INTERNATIONAL RELATIONS . 126
   Robert Leigh

NEW TECHNIQUES OF WAR AND NATIONAL POLICIES 144
   Bernard Brodie

MODERN TECHNOLOGY AND THE WORLD ORDER 174
   Quincy Wright

INDEX 199

INTRODUCTORY IDEAS ON INVENTIONS
AND THE STATE

By WILLIAM FIELDING OGBURN

THE purpose of this introduction is to develop a possible frame of reference for the reader of the chapters, varying in approach and range, which constitute the text of this book. The development of this frame of reference consists in the exposition of three themes. The three movements described have existed throughout all history, and in each a crisis exists at the present time. They are the shifts in the relative power of states, the evolution of states in geographical size, and the pursuit of peace. All three movements are related to and affected by technology. The presentation is wholly introductory and consists of the presentation of ideas and the indication of significances rather than the drawing of conclusions and the presentation of evidence.

THE RANKING OF POWERS

We may begin with a consideration of the ranking of states on the basis of their military power. In a world in which war is frequent, nations have a ranking order of power. They are like the chickens studied by biologists, which are found to have a definite pecking order when a feed pan is set down among them. The rank is perhaps not so definite among nations as it is among chickens, for the competition even in peacetime is not settled to the agreement of all concerned. The new inventions and population changes cause shifts in ranking after periods of struggle. For example, Britain fought it out with Spain on the seas in the sixteenth century and in the eighteenth and nineteenth century again with France. Britain's rank in the order of power was top during the nineteenth century.

Britain's top position was strengthened by her early acquisition of the steam engine and of modern methods of steelmaking. These inventions were applied to her navy and to her merchant ships. Her trading vessels carried the products of her factories to various parts of the world and brought back foods and raw materials. Britain, about the size of the state of Oregon, was thus enabled to support a population of forty-five million, whereas in 1800 her population was only ten million. The Industrial Revolution, produced by steam and steel, occurred first in Britain and is credited with strengthening her navy and her finances and increasing her population.

Inventions have a way of spreading after a time from one part of the world to another. But the use of coal in engines and the making of steel from iron ore cannot be done just anywhere. Coal mines are required, with iron mines not too far away. These requisites of military might are found in the United States, Russia, India, northern China and Manchuria, Germany, and, to a certain extent, in France, Poland, and Japan, but not so satisfactorily in other countries of Europe or in South and Central America. The use of steam engines and the making of steel spread from Britain to Germany, the United States, and Japan. These techniques are spreading, later, to the Soviet Union and will be adopted by India and China. Germany, the United States, and Japan became great powers. Indeed, Germany may be said to have challenged Britain's rank as a power.

Steam and steel do not alone produce a nation high in the rank of power. Belgium had steel mills, but not many; and her population was small. Also an area to be the seat of a great military power must have political coherence. The western and central parts of the continent of Europe have both coal and iron. If the peoples of this area had had political unity, the rank of this area as a power would be greater. Continental Europe may yet acquire the necessary political unity to become a great power.

One of the problems of policy, for non-Continental European powers, arising from the spread of steam and steel to Europe, is whether to encourage the continuance of a Europe made up of many small states or whether to favor consolidation. Consolidation would mean a stronger ally if the alliance could be guaranteed to last. The defeat of Germany had the effect of preventing a Europe more tightly organized around Germany as a center. There may be some fear on the part of other powers that a consolidated Europe might become too strong a power.

The Industrial Revolution is beginning to revolutionize the great area just east of Europe. The Soviet Union is organized politically and has both coal and iron and a large population. Indeed, with her heavy industries only partially developed and with her nationalism strongly assertive from the second World War, Russia is already high in the rank of powers.

An interesting question is whether the acquisition of steam and steel makes a nation warlike. Sometime in the near future India and China will have much production done by mechanical power in mass amounts from assembly lines. Will these two relatively peaceful peoples then become fighting states?

The question seems at least doctrinaire if not absurd, for is it not the will of a people and not steam power that makes them fight? And the will of a people is subject to persuasion. We shall not attempt to answer the question; and, of course, it cannot be answered definitively. But the idea may be a very important one, and we should like to present enough discussion to show that the question is not absurd in view of the probabilities in the practical world. The idea that industrial revolution may make a state warlike is really a question of the response of a people to machines which hold out the prospects of increasing wealth, which in turn calls for a search for ever more raw materials and for expanding markets. Both Japan and Germany became aggressor nations after they began to use steam in large amounts. Britain was, however, a relatively peaceful nation after she became industrialized. There were few, though, to challenge her supremacy. Nor has the highly industrialized United States been an aggressor nation. Although she was in the last two world wars, she entered late. The United States has had territory, natural resources in abundance, a small population, and no near-by challengers.

The theory that an industrial revolution may fan the spark of war into flames is based upon a sequence of attitudes, optimism, confidence, and aggressiveness that is found in many situations. We shall present first this theory independent of international relations.

First is the attitude of optimism that often comes with a sudden increase of wealth. The fact that rapidly growing cities are optimistic has been frequently observed. Cities that double their population in a decade are places in which incomes expand quickly. Among nations the agricultural states are relatively poor compared to the industrialized ones; and, when a nation whose occupations are largely farming and handicraft becomes possessed of power-driven factories that turn out products in profusion, the leadership, industrial and political, is likely to be optimistic.

The optimistic attitude is frequently correlated with the spirit of confidence, for optimism is often a result of achievement. A ruler or a political party claims credit for good times, though they be due to the forces of the business cycle or to the weather. Newly industrialized nations, like new cities, tend to have confidence.

Furthermore, these new and large rewards come as a result of initiative ("The early bird catches the worm"); and expanding factories, transportation systems, and merchandising establishments are the products of enterprise. So with optimism and confidence goes aggressiveness.

This aggressiveness need not display itself in war. It does not in cities, of course. When it does, we call it "aggression." But newly industrialized nations feel many needs—for raw materials, for new areas to exploit, for favorable trading conditions, for additional markets, and, in general, for expansion. It is sometimes easy for these needs to lead to war, particularly where war is in the national tradition.

The foregoing theory is hardly well enough established to forecast a warlike India or a China on the march for conquest when they become industrialized, or a more militant Russia when her heavy industries become greatly expanded after several more successful five-year plans. But such a contingency should be contemplated. This sequence of attitudes of optimism, confidence, and aggressiveness have been witnessed in Chicago, Seattle, and Los Angeles, on the Pacific Coast, and in Texas, Germany, Japan, and Britain. It may well be expected in India and China. New struggles for position in the ranking of powers may follow the spread of the power inventions.

Policies are generally based not upon such long-run forecasts but upon more immediate issues. Logically, a policy of a large, highly industrialized power state that wished to maintain its rank at the top would be to try to prevent the industrialization of a large, populous, potentially rival state. Britain, however, did not try to prevent the industrialization of Germany or of the United States. On the contrary, she advanced India on the road to mechanization. Indeed, the policy of such states is rather that of exporting technology. Britain helped finance the economic development of the United States. Such foreign investments are the source of immediate income to the investors, and such interests far outweigh the fear of the growth of a rival and challenger. Even if the policy of a state should be to prevent the industrialization of a potential rival, as, for instance, Russia or China, such a policy could not be successful, though it might cause a little delay in the process.

For a large industrialized power the spread of blast furnaces to small states presents little challenge. On the other hand, if the small states of an area unite, they may become a danger. Britain was aware of such a danger on the European continent. If Britain wants a union of western European states now, it is probably as an ally against a much stronger power or as a zone of security. If the Germans had won in the second World War, there would probably have been a good deal of integration of the various European states around Germany at the center. The combination might have been a very strong one. Indeed, there seems to be some fear from those that fought Germany in two world wars that, if a European union is formed, it will be dominated by a Germany which may turn aggressor again. Others view the struggle between Russia and the Anglo-Saxons as a fight for control of a united Europe; at the same time there are forces operating to split Europe in two, one part leaning toward Russia and the other toward Britain and the United States—a split which might prove costly in economic terms.

Policies of division or union in India and China have not been discussed. India, united under British rule, later became divided. China, which has had a long history of unity, probably could not be permanently so easily divided. On the other hand, China is not knitted closely together by the contact inventions—and hers is a system with a very great loyalty to family, possibly a priority over loyalty to the state—and, in fact, is divided now by civil war.

The military power of a country depends not upon mechanization alone but, among other factors, on population. Manpower is still a source of fighting strength. But technology affects the supply of manpower also. In the past the spread of the Industrial Revolution into a country has been accompanied by an increase in population, as was the case in Britain, in Germany, and in Japan. A natural question then is: "Will the expansion of power-driven industries in Russia stimulate an unusual increase in population; and, if so, how much will the population be increased?" This same question may be asked about India and about China, in which countries the populations are already large.

Further inquiry into this question of population increase accompanying industrialization suggests a breakdown of the problem into the influences that affect the balance of the birth rate and the death rate. The death rate was lowered in Germany and in England by sanitation and medical progress as well as by the growth of factories. Hospitals and plumbing can be diffused into various countries more easily than blast furnaces and, indeed, without them. So the forces operating for the reduction of the death rate have preceded in a measure the industrialization forces. The death rates in India and in Russia have decreased for these reasons, and this decline has already meant an unusual rate of population increase in these countries. Thus the forces associated with the coming of the Industrial Revolution to a country, which affect population growth through the lowered death rate, increase the strength of such industrialized nations as military powers.

Later, however, the spurt of population growth of newly industrialized states has lessened, and these states in maturity face a population decline. The slowing of the increase in population is due to a decreasing birth rate, particularly in cities. The reduced birth rate has been the result of birth control, which rests in part on the invention of contraceptives—simple inventions but vastly important in social consequences. While historically a rise in population growth due to industrialization and its accompaniments has preceded a fall in population growth due to birth control, it does not appear that this sequence is inevitable for the areas to be industrialized in the future. It is possible that the birth-control inventions could precede rather than follow the diffusion of the inventions of steam and steel. There is, however, no statistical evidence to indicate that this is likely to occur.

The influence of contraceptives on the ranking of powers may be very great, though they are, perhaps, not quite comparable to that of the power inventions.

It appears that the birth-control inventions are about to create in western Europe and in the United States either stationary populations or declining ones. The spread of contraceptives into the Soviet Union and to the Slavic peoples of eastern Europe has not gone very far, and before their wide adoption a considerable growth of the population even without industrialization is to be expected over the next thirty or forty years. Hence this technological influence favors the relatively greater rise of the Soviet Union as a military power.

There are, of course, many other technological influences, such as the airplane, that affect the ranking of powers, but these rest on a foundation of heavy industries. Finally, it is to be noted at the present time that the two leading great powers, the Soviet Union and the United States, are both large in area and in population. We raise the question as to whether at this stage of history the top-ranking powers can be other than very large ones.

IDEAS ON INVENTIONS AND THE STATE

THE GROWTH OF STATES IN SIZE

We now arrive in our introductory outline at another great phenomenon of history—the tendency of political units to grow larger. We wish to inquire how this trend is likely to operate in the near future. The question is particularly interesting at this time because of expressed desire of many observers, who want to avoid the destruction of an atomic war, for a world government—one large political unit encompassing the earth.

The trend toward larger political units is observable since preliterate times. The political groups of the American Indians before the advent of the white man and the horse inhabited quite small areas, though there was a good deal of territory included in each of the empires of the Mayas, the Incas, and the Aztecs. Before the Treaty of Westphalia there were nine hundred sovereign states among the Germanic peoples, which afterward were reduced to three hundred and fifty. When the Germanic Confederation was founded in 1815, the number was thirty-six; finally, in 1871 there was only one. Spain, France, Britain, Italy, Russia, and the United States are all unions of smaller political units. The same area, thus, tends in the long run to have fewer states.

These political entities may be thought of as of two types. One is the empire, held together generally by force, often attained by extensive conquests due to military superiority over the conquered peoples. The other is a nation with greater coherence and often less heterogeneity in language, ethnic stock, and customs.

The growth in size of both empire and nation has been achieved generally by military force, though the size has become greater also at times by the marriage of rulers and by federations based on agreement. Even when the Thirteen Colonies combined by agreement to form the United States, they sought strength in unification against possible military aggression from the outside.

In the expansion of states by conquest, technology plays a role, as does the size of the army and the quality of its courage. For instance, in the acquisition of colonial empires by Spain, France, and Britain in the sixteenth and seventeenth centuries, after the development of the boat and the compass, their superior technological equipment as compared with that of the natives made the conquest relatively easy. The advantage of the western Europeans in metals, horses, and gunpowder enabled vast empires to be created by conquests over peoples with only weapons of stone and wood, much inferior to guns and armor.

Conquests are not always enduring. Empires dissolve and states are split by civil war. So the growth of political units in size is met by reverses from time to time. The break-up of empires in particular is due to the weakness of the cohesive forces and to a rise in power of some coherent part of the empire. This dividing of empires is to be seen not as a trend but as variations around a trend.

An interesting question is the part played by transportation and, lately, by communication inventions in the evolution of states in size. Where transportation of humans is accomplished solely by their own muscle, the state cannot be very large; though, with the boat and waterways and with good roads or paths, the area of a state can be considerably enlarged. The addition of sails to boats and the domestication of the horse make still larger states possible. Indeed, very large empires have been built with the aid of sailboats and the horse. The steamboat has increased the possibility of great empires based upon sea power, while the railroad has helped in making more cohesive large nations of land power. We are naturally curious as to whether the airplane will be used for further increasing the size of the nation or empire.

The relationship of transportation to the size of political areas is not so simple as is implied in the preceding paragraphs and needs further analysis. We have already indicated that thinking on this subject must continually differentiate two concepts: the unstable empire built upon conquest but with not enough solidarity to endure without force and the more stable nation with many linkages other than force holding the peoples of the nation together. In either case transportation inventions are only means, which may or may not be used for the enlargement of the area. When the transportation techniques used are poor, such as human muscle, the nation or empire cannot be very large. The stage of the transportation systems sets a limit somewhere on size. On the other hand, with big ships, horses, and railroads, larger enduring nations are possible. Thus the stage of the transportation system makes states of varying sizes possible, depending upon the transportation inventions in use.

Since the transportation inventions are only a tool, an improvement in transportation is not automatically accompanied by an increase in the area of a state. An increase in the speed of railroad trains of 10 per cent is not automatically followed by an increase in area of the state of 10 per cent. Both small nations and large nations have railroads. Then, too, there are many other factors affecting the growth of states in size than the transportation inventions. One of these is wars of conquest. Where the differential in the tools of war is very great between the contestants, large areas may be brought under one rule. But first there must have been a war of conquest.

Another reason why transportational development is not soon followed by the increase in the size of states is the phenomenon of the resistance of political boundary lines to change. Over very long periods of time there is a correlation between transportation and size of political units, which were much smaller in Europe twenty-five hundred years ago than now. This is obvious, yet the point is important. Over short periods of time, perhaps hundreds of years, the correlation is not so clear. One reason is the resistance of political boundary lines to change. For instance, in the United States the political boundaries of counties, cities, and states when first determined bore a closer relation to economic and cultural conditions than at present. Now the economic city is larger than the political city, and we call it "the metropolitan area." County lines have not the social significance they had in the days of the horse and buggy, and many economic regions in the United States are much bigger than the states. A review of changes of boundary lines in Europe over the past several hundred years shows that most of the changes occur after wars. Therefore, in peacetime we should not expect transportation systems to be very effective in changing the boundaries of states. The influence, therefore, of the transportation inventions—which are only media—on the size of states would be effective only after a considerable lag, perhaps measured in hundreds of years.

When we speak of the evolution of nations in size, we mean durable nations, not transient empires. And when a one-world government is spoken of, it is an effective government that is wanted, not one that will be split by civil war or by secession.

The durability of a nation is a function of cohesive ties. What are these forces of cohesion? They are the magnetic force of common interests; but, to be felt and made known as common to the people of a community, there must be communication through contacts. Over a large area where the face-to-face contacts of a single person are with only a small fraction of the population, contacts are made with the aid of the transportation inventions or by the use of the communication devices. In modern times a great agency of communication is the printing press, the use of its products depending upon literacy.

These various contact inventions make for homogeneity through imitation, social pressure, intermarriage, trade, mass production, dress, topics of conversation, etc. It takes time for these similarities to occur. Religious differences, for instance, are very slow to break down. Hindus and Moslems living side by side have killed each other. More difficult to obtain is the cohesion of heterogeneous peoples having different languages, religions, customs, traditions, heroes, and loyalties.

The contact inventions are necessary, then, for the cohesiveness of peoples living over a large area. This is not to say that homogeneous groups may not have grave dissension. There may be religious differences, class friction, and economic conflicts in an area with many contact inventions. Indeed, the communication inventions are only tools which may be used for various purposes, for creating disruption as well as consensus. But, even when these inventions are used to foster homogeneity, there is delay due to resistances of race, of skin color, of religion, and of economic conflict.

We conclude that extensive use of the many contact inventions makes possible a greater solidarity of a large nation, in much the same way in which the transportation inventions, together with the military ones, make possible nations with larger boundaries.

The question that follows this analysis concerns the significance of this theory for the present situation. In the airplane, which is still evolving, we have a transportation vehicle that is quite extraordinary as compared to ship, railroad, and automobile in its ability to cover immense distances with tremendous speeds. It would seem to make possible, when its use becomes extensive, a very large political unit, perhaps as large as the earth's surface. The domestication of the horse did not lead at once to the empire of Genghis Khan, about one-fifth of the land area of this planet.

Modern war inventions also make possible a very large nation. The atomic bomb, the air bomber, and the tank are very powerful weapons. The superiority of a state possessing them over a state not having them is great indeed. Speaking quite generally, does it not now appear possible for one state after one or more wars to conquer the world?

If these suggestions seem fantastic, the more modest claim that the new transportation inventions and the new war inventions make possible a very large political unit does not appear to be exaggerated. Small nations are quite at the mercy of the large mechanized ones. Twice the Germans made a bid by war for a larger territory. Without defeat we do not know how extensive their control might have been. Extensive conquest seems often to lead more readily and first to the empire type of political structure which has less inherent stability than a unified state.

If, then, a world government is possible by virtue of the transportation and wartime inventions, we may ask whether this world structure can be administered and controlled successfully. The heterogeneity of the peoples of the world is very great, but so was the heterogeneity of the Roman Empire and of the British. To reduce the heterogeneity into the degree of homogeneity required for a nation, the contact inventions are needed, for they make possible the spread of similarities.

There do exist now a wonderful assortment of contact inventions comprising the airplane, radio, television, facsimile, telephone, teletype, and printing press. The effective reduction of heterogeneity depends not only upon their existence but upon the extent of their use and to the amount of resistance of localisms to their impact. The statistics on telephone, airplane, automobile, and radio sets show much less use of these in other parts of the world than in the United States. Furthermore, the varieties of language, religion, and the extent of illiteracy argue for the resistance to the spread of uniformities for a long time to come. The various states of Europe, although now fewer in number than a thousand years ago, are still not united into one single state. As important in these considerations, also, is the strength of local power groups which we now call "nations." They have the potentialities by virtue of their ability in collective action to break away from a world state.

If, then, a durable world state seems remote, the forces which help to produce the very large durable state are in existence. But, as we have seen, the existence of a set of contact inventions is not necessarily followed in a reasonably short time by an expansion in area of states. Yet these contact inventions are being used more and are more available to speed the evolution of states in size. Even the mechanized war inventions have been recently employed in two world wars in an effort to expand a large state. That the effort was unsuccessful for that particular state does not deny the fact of two world wars in a quarter of a century. Also we observe that, after the second World War, the top-ranking powers were larger than were the top-ranking powers before the first World War.

Before closing this theme of the evolution of political units in size, the question may be raised as to whether a new type of political unit may not be in the making. We have referred to two types—the nation and the empire. The possible emerging type may be a large nation with surrounding zones of influence. The large states want to have the near-by states friendly. As centers of dispersal of economic and cultural influence, these large states may integrate fairly closely, through the medium of the contact inventions, with the bordering friendly states into a regional grouping with the large state at the center. This may be done without any special formal political integration but with much the same functioning in international matters as if they were integrated politically.

This political arrangement of a large region may prove to be too unstable to be called a new type of political unit. Yet, even if it be not enduring, it may be a phase in the evolution of states in size.

However problematical the forecasts may be as to the growth of state in size, the existence of such a trend over the historical period indicates an important phenomenon as a frame of reference, set forth in this introduction, as a basis for the interpretation of the relationship of technology and international relations.

THE INCREASING DESTRUCTIVENESS OF WAR

There is a third phenomenon, of recent origin yet of great importance, on which some comment is needed as an introductory idea for the reading of the chapters which follow. The comment, though, may be brief. It is the vast devastation which wars now bring and which may be increased even more in future wars.

This increase in the destructiveness of wars is the result of science. Technology is applicable to war as well as to peaceful pursuits. So there are miracles of destruction as well as miracles of construction wrought by the marvels of science. These facts are well known. They are symbolized by the atomic bomb. But, before the atomic bomb, the chemical bombs were very destructive. Whole cities have been destroyed by them.

We have referred to the extreme devastation of modern war as contemporary rather than as characteristic of history. Some primitive peoples, however, have been almost exterminated by the superior war power, especially of the white peoples; and some European wars in the past have been very destructive, as was the Thirty Years' War.

But modern science has made the total mass of destruction vastly greater than ever before in history. We should, however, be looking toward the future, on this problem of the human cost of wars, rather than toward the past or the present.

A point to be remembered but often overlooked is that new inventions do not remain as they now are but evolve. Atomic fission is only about a decade old. Many new discoveries are to be expected in nuclear physics, though now we do not know what they may be. We already have prevision of long-range rockets, of guided missiles, of radiating dust, of bacteriological warfare, and of superior atom bombs. Other elements than the heavy-weight thorium and uranium may be used for explosion, fire, and radiation. We are sure that science will make the potential destructiveness of wars much greater in the future, though we do not know the details, provided we continue to follow the pursuit of war.

It is possible that science will also create a defense of some kind, mechanical or social, for this new offensive power. Historians tell us that eventually defense has always caught up with offense. The explanation of this tendency for offense and defense in war to come to a balance is found in the great power of the factor of demand in the inventive process. As inventions accumulate, we are able to invent almost anything we want to. This statement is not wholly true of course. We have been a long time trying to discover a cure for cancer. So we do not know absolutely that a defense will be found for the new war weapons. But, if defense does catch up with offense, it may be long delayed; and the costs of defense may be as great as, for instance, the dispersal of city populations, which involves a remaking of a large part of civilization.

The nature of mechanized warfare of the present and of the future has become so horrible to contemplate, and it seems so suicidal to wage such wars, that we naturally ask: "Why fight at all? Why not abolish war altogether?" The search for peace is not new. It has existed during all history through treaties, agreements, the resolution of conflicting interests, and the limitation of armaments. Today this search takes a more generalized form, in addition to the old procedure, of a peace movement to prevent war forever everywhere.

In the past the adjustment to new discoveries and inventions of metals, cutting tools, vehicles, and explosives has been to incorporate them into the warring activities. If precedents of history are followed, we shall use bacteria and radiating particles, rockets, and guided missiles in the wars to come. But using them in war is not the only adjustment to the new technologies. The adjustment to such lethal inventions could be to change our habit of going to war. So the effect of the new technology could be to abolish war. Certainly the effect has been to stimulate movements toward a lasting peace. The question, of course, is how effective such a movement would be.

The obstacles are very great even though the objective is sensible and desirable. Most difficult of these obstacles are the awareness of ruthless attacks and invasions of the past and fear of them in the future, remembrance of broken agreements, the great desire for the security thought to be afforded by military preparation, and the theory that the best defense is attack. Then there are such obstacles as conflicts of interest, particularly economic, the effectiveness of power in various international activities, and the tradition of prestige and glory. A contemplation of these resistances by those who have read their history carefully make them seem very difficult indeed to overcome.

Some have thought that a less difficult objective is some restriction of the use of these agents of destruction in warfare. We have tried to restrict the use of the atom bomb but have met so far with failure. But war, like all collective activity, has rules. In many wars of the past there have been rules against atrocities. Even with the breaking-down of codes today, we do in general conform to the rule of not killing prisoners. It may be that later we shall try again to prohibit the use of atomic bombs or set up a rule of not bombing cities which do not have military objectives within their borders, such as factories. Such agreements may be broken, of course, but not all new habits are established at once without fail.

Along with the attempts to restrict the use of atomic energy, there occurred a movement to preach peace into practice by persuasion, particularly through the motive of fear. Success of such a movement in the country of only one of the potential contestants would be dangerous without the development of a similar attitude in the other. This is not to say that education for peace is not a proper accompaniment to our efforts to abolish war.

The development of an international organization based upon such beginnings as are found in the League of Nations and in the United Nations is generally viewed as a more effective approach. However, the obstacles to attaining a world political unit, as recorded in a previous section, make one realize the magnitude of the task. Especially is it important to realize that the attainment of a single world political unit must be concerned with the processes of power.

A world federation of states with considerable power still has the problem of disruption, due to heterogeneity of interests, the weakness of the agencies of cohesion, and the power of local groups with nationalistic traditions. The purpose of these remarks is, however, not to pass judgments or to reach conclusions but rather to indicate the various possible effects of the new inventions on the attempts to find peace.

Another effort to adjust to the new technology of war is to try to postpone war as long as possible without attempting to set up at once an effective organization to abolish war forever. With the present geographical distribution of bipolar power, if the conflict of national and ideological interests could be workably adjusted and a greater sense of security from attack could be had and guarded, war might be postponed for a long time. Perhaps the most serious difficulty in maintaining a very long peace is the rise of new powers among the states and the decline of old ones. These shifts often occur, as we have seen, with new technological developments and necessitate changes in boundaries and expansions in areas. These changes have always been difficult to handle by the peaceful methods of negotiation. The effort to postpone war would make use of the familiar historical skills with which states of the past have dealt with one another. The skills which have failed in the past (though they have succeeded for fairly long periods) may fail again in the future. The idea this time, though, is to utilize the time gained by the postponement of war to build up new international organizations for peace, for it will probably take some time to give them the strength needed.

In conclusion, then, one social effect of the new destructive agencies of war is to stimulate several different movements to avoid the great destructiveness of war: restriction of weapons, the adoption of peace through fear and persuasion, strengthening the United Nations, a world federation, a one-world government by conquest, and a postponement of war to gain time to strengthen the movement for peace. However these various movements may develop, the impact of the destructive weapons is to increase greatly the efforts for peace.

The chapters which follow deal in varying degrees of emphasis and approach with contemporary crises in international relations, each one of which, however, is concerned with the three themes common to history, set forth in this introductory frame of reference; namely, the shifts in the ranking of powers, the growth of states in size, and the movement for peace.

THE PROCESS OF ADJUSTMENT TO NEW INVENTIONS

By WILLIAM FIELDING OGBURN

THE subject of international relations is often presented in terms of policies. These policies are generally seen in terms of choice, will, and action by leaders. Bismarck's policy was one of moderation as compared to that of Kaiser Wilhelm. Or Bismarck chose to wage war. Stories of alliances, of national commitments, and of diplomatic strategy are dramatic accounts of human behavior. Then, too, the explanations of international action are frequently in terms of principles. The enemy wants to enslave the world; or we wish to make it safe for democracy.

Into such an atmosphere technology appears as a strange intrusion. Against the mighty force of morals it seems incidental rather than a determining force to be reckoned with seriously. For is not an invention an instrument to do man's bidding for such ends as he chooses?

Yet few would doubt that the early acquisition of steam power by the British before other states acquired it helped them to become the leading world power of the nineteenth century and thereby made the task of British diplomacy much easier. Britain's steel mills, with their products for peace and for war, enabled her to spread much more effectively the ways of European civilization into Africa and southern and southeastern Asia. Yet we are disposed to give credit to Gladstone, or even to Queen Victoria. Another illustration is the praise we extend to Columbus for the discovery of America. Yet without the new large boats and their equipment, this continent would not have been discovered from Europe; and with such boats, if Columbus had not lived, some other adventurous navigator would have made the discovery. No one thinks of attributing the discovery of America to a boat, though.

We may say, then, that technology makes possible certain human achievements, and we may also admit that without such material aids these achievements would not be possible. But there are other ways in which invention affects human action. The purpose of this chapter is to inquire into these processes.

ADJUSTMENT TO NEW INVENTIONS

We begin by pointing out a restriction of the subject. We are concerned here only with how invention and science affect international relations and not with how international relations affects science and invention. Though we recognize that international relations, to wit, war, was a factor in developing the submarine, for instance, a more proper concern under this limitation would be with how the submarine affected international relations, to wit, Germany's relations with Britain, whose ships could, without the submarine, blockade the Baltic Sea.

Furthermore, when it is found that technology affects international relations, it is not to be implied that no other factor is of any influence. Several causes often exist, of which only one is a new invention. Thus the development of heavy industry, driven with mechanical power, in the Soviet Union will increase her might as a state. But so will the growth of her population of military age, which will occur at the same time that her factory production will be increased. The problem here, however, is to trace out the processes of one factor, technology, and not to appraise the relative strength of each of the many factors involved.

Quite a problem in analysis is what to do with the factor that does not change. For instance, shall we credit Britain's increase as a power in the nineteenth century to her coal mines? But the island had coal when it was not a power, as when the Romans or the Normans occupied it. Coal only becomes useful when there are steam engines in which to burn it. The coming of the steam engine, not coal, is the variable which explains the increase of Britain as a power in the nineteenth century.

The phenomenon we seek to explain is a variable, namely, a change in Britain's position as a power. A change must be explained in terms of a change. Thus the reader is reading this page not because there is oxygen in the air but for some other reason. The necessity of the oxygen in reading is apparent, but it is useless as an explanation of why a reader is reading this page instead of attending a theater, say, or reading something else.

Returning to the illustration of coal, while it has been a constant over time in Britain and hence could not explain a change in her position, coal is not a constant between two nations. Thus, France has little coal and Germany has much; hence coal is a factor in explaining why Germany is a greater power than France. In these illustrations coal is a variable over space but not over time.

An interesting question is whether human nature should be considered a constant. Sometimes it is and sometimes it is not. Between individuals there is great variation in some traits—desire for power, for instance. But between large populations, perhaps, the percentage of the population that desire power may be about the same.

If a new invention calls forth the same response from human beings in the societies being compared which use it, we think of the new invention, a variable, as a causative factor and not human behavior, which is in this situation a constant. Thus, in all cities, automobiles have developed suburbs. Human beings in all cities want more space in which to live. The desire for more space is a constant, then, from one large city to another. Hence we do not say that the desire for space caused the suburbs. The desire for space is a variable, though, between the open country and the city. Ranchers do not desire more space in which to live and do not use the automobile for that purpose.

Inventions are made relatively suddenly and are dropped, so to speak, into a social situation. Often this social situation is the same as to basic human attitudes before the invention occurs and after the invention is adopted. So we do not say that the attitude is a factor in explaining a change following the invention, because the attitude is a constant. These social situations may vary, though, from one country to another. Thus, the appearance of contraceptives in China may not lead to the same results as did their appearance in Protestant western Europe, for attitudes on the Chinese desire for children is different, with their ancestor worship and their familial institutions. So also the effect of the airplane on international relations would be quite different in a world situation which is not warlike from what it is in a world in which a power struggle is going on.

In international relations the variables often stressed are leaders, personalities, social movements, and organizations. These are important variables in explaining particular actions and specific achievements. But because of their significance the variations of the technological factors should not be obscured. The purpose of this book is to bring out the more important of these.

One reason technological factors are obscured is that causes appear in a sequence like the links of a chain, and the link signifying the factor of technology is often somewhat removed and not so close to the change being explained as is the leader of a movement or the head of an organization. Thus, we observed the prime minister of the United Kingdom, as World War II came to a close, repeatedly advancing the interests of France in international conferences. But back of this British policy we note the invention of the rocket carrying an explosive and the airplane, both of which have rendered water barriers to Britain less effective and have increased the value of defense in depth. Britain becomes increasingly eager for a strong and a friendly France. Thus, the inclusion of France in many postwar actions is caused first by the political leaders, but also a cause back of that is the changed nature of war occasioned by new transportation inventions. This is not to say that there were not other factors or that Britain has not wanted the support of France long before these inventions of the airplane. It is rather that the increased need of Britain for France is caused by a change in technology.

One final observation should be made on the idea of inevitability, often implied in speaking of the influence of an invention. It is as though men had no choice in the matter. Thus, we think of the invention of gunpowder as inevitably changing the course of feudalism. But, it may be argued, men had the "choice" of using the explosive to propel missiles. The Chinese did not so use it. In the past, where the effect of invention in history has already occurred, we more readily admit inevitability than we do in looking to the future, where we seem to have choice, for instance, as to what we shall do about using the atomic bomb. We are using the word "choice" as it is popularly used and shall here not go beyond this conception. It may be preferable in referring to the future to speak of "adjustment to technology" rather than to the "effect of technology."

Inevitability and choice are a dichotomy of extremes. A more realistic approach is to think in terms of degrees of a continuum rather than of two extreme categories. Hence, it is preferable to think of the influences of invention in terms of probabilities. A good way of visualizing probabilities of a relationship of two variables is in terms of a correlation table, in which the coefficient may vary from zero to one, and, when it does, there are other factors involved which if unknown may carry the idea of chance or choice. It does not appear necessary that ideas of free will complicate the analysis in the paragraphs which follow.

THE FIRST EFFECTS OF AN INVENTION

Let us start our inquiry with the fact of an invention. A new invention is made. It is here. In what ways will civilization be different because of it?

The first stage of inventional influence is in its use. It should be observed, however, that not every invention is used. Probably more than 90 per cent of them are not used. There appears to be a "choice" as to whether we shall make use of a scientific discovery or not. We did not choose to use poison gas in World War II. In other cases, where the demand is strong, continuous, and widely spread, the use is assured, as in the case of the discovery of anesthetics. All of us, except a few eccentrics, want to avoid pain.

Once a significant invention is widely used, there follow changes in the habits of the users. Steamships change the habits of sailors. So an early stage in the social effects of an invention is changes in the habits of users.

For an invention to be used, it must be produced. So, parallel with these changes due to use, there occur changes due to production. If we decide to use the atom bomb, new types of factors are set up. Using an invention makes changes due to its production inevitable, though there are some choices, as in the location of factories or in the materials to be used. The impact of an invention upon consumers and producers is generally recognized.

DERIVATIVE INFLUENCES

That the impact of inventions upon society extends beyond their influence upon consumers and producers is not generally appreciated. The influence of the long-range air bomber does not cease with its changes in the usages of warfare. It extends beyond and affects the foreign policies of states during peacetime. This influence on foreign policies is derived from its use and is therefore called a "derivative influence."

Derivative influences of science flow not only from users but also from producers. For instance, the changes in the production of explosives due to atomic fission have a derivative influence upon the relation of small states or outlying areas, with possible or actual uranium deposits, to great powers making atomic bombs. The competition for atomic bombs thus leads through the first stage of production to rivalries in the search for raw materials—a derivative effect from the production of the invention.

ADJUSTMENT TO NEW INVENTIONS

WHY THERE ARE DERIVATIVE EFFECTS

The reason derivative influences spread from users and producers to social institutions is the existence of interconnections between the parts of civilization. Our modern culture is put together more like a clock, with its interrelationships of parts, than it is, let us say, like a chain, where some links may be changed without greatly affecting the whole. In a total war today almost every institution, every organization, is affected, so closely interconnected are the different parts of modern civilization.

Hence, if an invention through its use changes one part of our social organization, its influence does not stop there but extends toward the other parts of our social order which are connected with it. For instance, in societies, travel is interconnected with a system of lodgings. When one travels a long distance, one must have a place to spend the night away from home. If the method of travel which depends upon time schedules and a few fixed tracks is changed by the addition of the private automobile, independent of schedules and for which there are many different highways, a change in the system of lodging is inevitable, whether it be tourist camps, motels, or guest homes. Once we decide to use private automobiles for traveling long distances, the derivative change in the hotel system follows.

Sometimes the linkages between the parts of the social order are not so strong as that between travel and inns, in which case the derivative effect is not so certain. A rather weak linkage exists, for instance, between the transportation system and resettlement—not so strong as between transportation and temporary lodgings. The addition to overseas transportation of fast and large steamships with regular schedules was accompanied by an increase in emigration from Europe to America; but such a derivative effect as migration does not appear to follow inevitably solely because of the new invention of the steamboat. For, later, this immigration was stopped while the steamboats continued to run; nor did immigration occur in transportation across the Pacific Ocean. Thus it is not at all certain that resettlement will be a derivative influence of transportation changes.

The reason resettlement is not always a derivative effect of a new transportation invention is that transportation is only one of many factors in peoples' determining to change their home. Other factors are economic opportunity, population pressure, the fluctuations of the business cycle, and political barriers. Most social phenomena, like immigration, are the products of many different variables.

CONVERGENCE

Often several of these variables which operate to produce a social change are influences from several different inventions. The influences of these inventions are said to converge to bring about a result. A good illustration is the widening differential between the small powers and the large ones since the second World War. This is one of the effects of the air bomber. Small countries with few heavy industries cannot well provide the necessary defenses in fighter planes and antiaircraft guns to stop a great power's large destructive fleet of bombers. Furthermore, the development of the airplane is achieved much better in states with a great expanse of territory, which a small state does not have. With the ability of the air bomber to hit military objectives anywhere, the resistance of a small state is greatly weakened.

The invention of the armored tank has the same general effect on widening the comparative military strengths of small and large states. So also do rockets and guided projectiles, especially if there are many cities in the small state. A great power can have more scientific laboratories and greater use of mass production. There then is the convergence of the influence of many different inventions to make the great power stronger and the little power weaker. In this case the influences of these different converging inventions is additive. In convergence the contribution of any invention to a social change is a fraction.

SUCCESSIVE DERIVATIVES

We have shown that the effect of an invention does not stop with its uses. Nor does it stop with its first derivative influence. It proceeds to still other linked institutions. The process of successive derivative influences is much like the game of billiards when the cue ball strikes another, which in turn hits still another, and so on.

The invention of the cotton gin, for example, by removing a bottleneck to cotton utilization, led to increased production of cotton in the southern states by an expansion of slave labor, since the world demand for cotton cloth from the mills of England was very great. There followed a struggle for new slave territory in the western states about ready to be admitted to the Union as states. This struggle for political power between the northern and southern states accentuated the issue of a high tariff versus free trade, since the South could export more cotton with free trade and since the industries of the

North could grow faster under the protection of a tariff. This struggle reached a climax in the War between the States. There were, then, a succession of derivative influences following the invention of the cotton gin.

It seems absurd to imply that the invention of the cotton gin caused the war of 1860–64. But such is not the implication. The cotton gin was only one factor, large or small, in a series of successive convergences of derivative influences, such as the expanding market for textiles from British factories, the opening of new lands for settlement, the development of new factories in northern states, etc.

The proportional influence of the cotton gin becomes smaller as new influences are added in successive convergences. If an inventional influence is one in three other influences on convergence No. 1, and the influence of convergence No. 1 is one in four other influences on convergence No. 2, then the invention's influence is only one in seven on the second convergence. So the proportional influence of an invention diminishes through a succession of derivatives.

It is not customary to think of an invention like the cotton gin of the 1800's as having an influence on the tariff of the 1850's, for the invention of the gin is far removed not only in time but in successive convergences. Nevertheless, we may ask the pertinent question: "If the cotton gin had never been invented, would the tensions between the northern and southern states have reached an intensity great enough to start a conflagration of war?" The removal of an invention from society, if no substitute is provided, would show how far-reaching are its derivative influences.

RESISTANCES TO TECHNOLOGICAL INFLUENCES

Convergence is a phenomenon of social change. In a stationary society its analogue would be a pattern of linked parts of society. The family as an institution is linked to education, to production, to protection, etc. The appearance of a new invention in a system of linked material objects, institutions, and habits may modify the system, that is, the system adjusts to the invention.

These adjustments do not take place easily. Sometimes the pattern of a culture cannot assimilate a new invention. An area without coal and iron cannot assimilate the blast furnace, though it could buy the products of the Industrial Revolution. Japan could incorporate into its system the steam and steel complex, but the Australian aborigine could not. In other cases assimilation may be readily accomplished.

To adopt the jet fighter plane by a country engaged in the war production of planes was not difficult.

An invention is, then, like a seed which may fall on different kinds of soil. The soils that are too sandy, too wet, too dry, or too rocky may be said to offer resistances to the growth from the seed. So there are obstacles to the adoption of inventions. A law was passed in Hungary in 1523 to prevent the use of four-wheeled coaches, since there was fear that the training of cavalry would be less effective. It should be observed that eventually the people of Hungary did use coaches.

There are also resistances to the derivative influences, as in the case of inventions of local transportation which have spread the economic city beyond the boundaries of the political city. There is great resistance to extending outward the political boundaries of an expanding city.

Similarly, the influence of various transportation, communication, and military inventions is to spread the influence of a state, which is a great center of dispersal, outward to the small border states, sometimes called a "zone of influence." But the influence of large states over the small neighboring political units is resisted. Any loss of sovereignty or change of boundary lines particularly is expected to be resisted. There are many linkages of different parts of a state with its political structure.

LAGS

This resistance, which inventions and their influences meet, means delays in time in the spread of technological effects on society. One such delay is that of straightening highways and rail tracks to permit the speeds which new engines yield. The linkage is close, but the adjustment to the new speeds lags.

Some of these lags are very long indeed. The uniting of the European states economically or politically has lagged a long time after the inventions of production and transportation have made it possible and desirable and long after the disadvantage of this lack of union is evident in comparison with large united areas like the United States and the U.S.S.R.

The long lag in yielding to the influence of technological developments has made the correlation between technological change and social change more difficult to see. An illustration is the counties in the United States. The political units were laid out in the days of horse-drawn transportation and when the technology of production was on farms fairly equably distributed. Now the administration of counties would probably be better and cheaper per capita if a state had five or ten counties instead of a hundred. If the county lines are not changed, they will become less and less functional, and the adjustments to the new technological developments will be made by grants-in-aid, new taxation procedures, and the shifting of functions· to states and cities. The long delays in adjustments obscure the correlation.

THE WEIGHT OF THE TECHNOLOGICAL FACTOR

We have now traced the main steps in the process of social changes flowing from inventions and scientific discoveries. But an analysis of the process is not an assessment of the importance of technology as compared with other factors. An analysis of ideational innovations would probably have shown somewhat similar processes. Regarding the relative importance of technological forces, a few remarks in the nature of theory will be made.

THE VARIABILITY OF MODERN TECHNOLOGY

One reason we think technology is important in international relations is its great variability. There are many new and important inventions occurring every decade: facsimile transmission, radio telephone, jet propulsion, rockets, helicopters, radar, television, photography, lithoprinting, plant hormones, alloys, atomic fission, and many others. Indeed, the number of inventions tends to grow exponentially.

The significance of the variability of invention lies in the fact that we do not consider a constant as a causal factor in change. It must be a variable that explains a variation. Thus a variation from sailing ships to steamships led to changes in British foreign policy. National interest is, of course, a factor in British foreign policy, but that is a constant, which was present both before and after the appearance of the steamship, and does not explain the changes.

Another constant in international relations, at least for a time, is the desire for national security. The new inventions of war give emphasis to the policy of the Soviet Union to obtain a zone of security around it. The ideological constant is the desire for security. The new inventions lead to policies regarding particular countries.

THE VARIATION IN IDEOLOGIES

Ideologies vary, too; and, in so far as they do, they must be given weight. We have no conclusive answer as to whether in modern times as many important ideological factors vary as do important technological factors. We have recently seen the rise of fascism and communism, important ideological developments. It should not be assumed, however, that fascism and communism originated independently of technological changes. In some cases the technological factor in the origin of ideologies or their variation is clear. The safety-first movement, incorporating the social invention of workmen's compensation, was occasioned by the invention of fast-moving metal machines and vehicles. It may also be argued that the idea of the federation of the Western nations arises in part because of the variation in the transportation and military inventions. The ideology of 'isolationism," so prominent in the United States, is being eliminated, by the airplane.

On the other side, ideologies cause changes in technology. The atom bomb, jet propulsion, and radar were creations of the war ideas. The influence of war on creating inventions is more the influence of demand arising from a social condition than the force of an ideology.

War is an illustration of a nontechnological factor that is not always a constant, not so much so as national interest and national security. The prospects of war vary from decade to decade and from one continent to another. Indeed, one foreign policy in which the people of the United States are deeply interested is to produce a more marked variation in this factor of war, that is, to eliminate it.

The foregoing discussion does not settle the question of the relative importance of technology but is rather an exploration of some aspects of the problem. In any case, the purpose of this paper is rather to describe the processes whereby technological change influences society.

SUMMARY

We may now summarize the processes of change instituted by the appearance of an invention in our culture. Society is different, first, because of the new habits of users and producers of the invention, assuming the invention meets a demand and is not rejected. This first step in the impact of technology upon civilization is common knowledge. But the effect of an invention is not restricted solely to its direct influence on its users and its producers. Institutions and ideologies may also make adjustments to the new habits of users and consumers. Thus an invention has a derivative influence upon social institutions indirectly through its users or producers. This derivative influence is often not recognized by casual observers because it is once removed from the invention. This observation is most commonly left unmade in the case of a chain of successive derivative influences. The phenomenon of derivative influences arises because of the intercorrelation of the parts of culture.

The derivative influence of any particular invention is often not appreciated because it is only one of many converging influences, many of which flow from other inventions, mechanical or social. In the case of successive derivative convergences of inventions, the influence of one early invention may be comparatively small.

Because of the intercorrelation of the parts of culture and the fact that many social phenomena exist because of the presence of many factors, the effects of inventions are resisted or delayed until a favorable situation develops. Sometimes the derivative influence of an invention requires for an adjustment an ideational or social invention.

All these processes may be observed in the influence of the inventions of steam and steel, aviation, and other means of transportation, the atom bomb and the mass-communications inventions, upon the ranking of powers, the federation of nations, spheres of influence, and diplomatic procedure.

TECHNOLOGY AND THE GROWTH
OF POLITICAL AREAS

By HORNELL HART

DURING all history and prehistory, man has been grappling with the problems of transportation and of government. He has been trying to learn to transport himself and his goods more quickly and more easily from place to place. He has also been attempting to organize governments and to exert social control more and more widely. The present paper seeks to explore some major relationships between these two aspects of cultural development, with a view to making possible more accurate prediction and more effective action. Specifically, this paper seeks light upon the following alternative questions relating to prediction and action in these fields.

1. Can future expansions of political areas be predicted from the emergence of individual transportational inventions? Have such developments as wheeled vehicles, domestication of horses, Roman roads and bridges, deep-sea navigation, the locomotive, the steamship, and the airplane been the decisive factors which have determined the course of political development? If so, is it possible to predict reliably and usefully the future effects of such inventions as the airplane and the prospective atomic-propelled space ship on international relations and on the possible development of world government?

2. Instead of regarding the individual transportational invention as the cause, and the predictive symptom, of subsequent political growth, do the facts of past cultural development require us to recognize such inventions as inseparable parts of technological progress, which must be studied as a whole before any reliable and useful predictions and principles of action can be derived?

3. If Question 2 is answered affirmatively, is it possible to define or to measure technological change in general in any such specific and reliable way as to describe its past developments accurately and to forecast its future influence?

4. On the basis of past relationships between technological progress and political growth, can world government be expected to emerge automatically in response to current technological developments?

5. If social controls cannot be expected to emerge automatically, but if future technological developments can be predicted reliably, is it possible to use social science effectively to promote the international adjustments which modern technology has made imperative?

The present paper cannot, of course, be expected to provide more than some initial insights toward the answering of such questions.

Successive stages in transportation may be differentiated primarily on the basis of types of power employed. The major types may be listed as (1) human muscles; (2) domesticated animals; (3) wind; (4) steam; (5) electricity; (6) oil engines; (7) jet propulsion; (8) atomic. Transportation is further differentiated in accordance with whether the power is applied to travel by land, by water, or by air. On the basis of these criteria, the body of this paper has been divided into chronological sections. After an exposition of available facts, an attempt will be made, in the final section, to present some tentative conclusions bearing upon the first three of the five questions listed above.

PRE-HORSE TRANSPORTATION AND POLITICAL DEVELOPMENT

Study of the prehistoric aspects of this problem is based on the general assumption that any statistically significant relations which can be demonstrated between the technologies and the political development of modern preliterate peoples can reasonably be assumed to have been true of the prehistoric peoples who had corresponding technologies.[1] To make such a study, two objective indexes are needed: first, a measure of political development applicable to modern primitive tribes and (by inference) to prehistoric peoples; second, objective evidence as to transportational developments among these peoples.

The political development of preliterate peoples can be measured in two different ways. One is to use the best estimates which are available as to the areas controlled by representative preliterate peoples at specified stages of technological development. This method will be employed later in comparing the rates at which political development has occurred at various prehistoric stages. A second method of measuring political development is based upon the fact that geographical political organizations, among any people, are built up by a serial process of compounding. A number of mother-child groups

1. For a factual exploration of this assumption see Hornell Hart and Donald L. Taylor, "Was There a Prehistoric Trend from Smaller to Larger Political Units?" *American Journal of Sociology*, XLIX (1944), 289–301.

may be organized into one household; a number of households may be organized into one local community or one clan; a number of clans or communities may be organized into one tribe or city; a number of tribes or cities may be organized into a district federation or a county; a number of such federations or counties may be organized into a state or nation; a number of states or nations may be organized into an empire or federated commonwealth; a number of empires and commonwealths might be organized into a regional, continental, or hemispheric union; and a number of these superstates might be organized into a world government. On the basis of this serial process of compounding, the political ratings shown in Table 1 have been derived.[2]

This table summarizes data as to political development and transportational advancement for the twelve preliterate peoples for whom the information is available. It will be seen that, for water transportation, the three tribes which were least developed politically had the crudest boats or rafts but that the largest boats, with matting sails, were possessed by two tribes in the middle group—the Haidas and the Samoans. The tribes with the greatest political expansion either had no boats or had relatively crude dugouts with no sails.

For land transportation, beasts of burden were possessed by two intermediate tribes (the Kazaks and the Hottentots, who had oxen) and by one advanced people (the Incas, who had llamas). On the highest political level as well as the lowest, most of the freight was transported by humans, with tumplines across the forehead. The most primitive peoples tended to leave load-carrying to the women,

---

2. While the political ratings given in Table 1 are, strictly speaking, indexes of complexity of organization rather than of area, it is clear that peoples with high indexes tend to control far larger territories than those with low indexes. This is true because a low index means that the group consists of only a few households or clans, each holding a very small territory, while a high index means that such small groups have been compounded and recompounded into tribes, districts, nations, and even empires. That this actually holds true is shown (pp. 34–36) by the facts about four peoples (three of whom are among those listed in Table 1), as summarized below:

Political Index	People	Approximate Area Controlled (In Square Miles)
20.............	Aranda	7,000
135.............	Iroquois	22,500
146.............	Aztecs	500,000
226.............	Incas	250,000

The correlation between the political indexes and the areas is by no means perfect, but it would seem to be fairly obvious. Moreover, under the definitions employed, it would be reasonably simple to estimate what would be the political index of an all-inclusive world government.

while the politically more developed were more likely to have professional porters. Only among the highest group, politically, did "important persons" have the privilege of being transported in litters, or in hammocks swung on poles, between human carriers.

The most striking difference between the transportation of the politically most advanced peoples and the other two groups was related to the roads. The Ganda, the Aztecs, and the Incas had elaborate systems of highways. That of the Incas was said to have been

TABLE 1*

TRANSPORTATION METHODS AND FACILITIES OF TWELVE PRELITERATE PEOPLES
AS DESCRIBED BY MURDOCK, GROUPED ACCORDING TO
POLITICAL DEVELOPMENT

POLITICAL RATINGS†	PEOPLES	OUTSTANDING TRANSPORTATIONAL METHODS AND FACILITIES	
		By Water	By Land
22.....	Tasmanians	Bark rafts, propelled by poles	No roads; women carry the freight
30.....	Witotos	Twenty-foot canoes; paddles	Women carry loads on heads or in baskets supported by tumplines
32.....	Crows	Rafts; no boats	Dog-drawn travois
28.....	Mean		
37.....	Haidas	Seventy-foot canoes; mat sails	
45.....	Kazaks		Camels; oxen with pack saddles; everyone rides horses
61.....	Hottentots		Oxen
75.....	Samoans	Sixty-foot outrigger canoes; mat sails	
55.....	Mean		
135.....	Iroquois	Canoes carry twenty men	Beaten trails; sleds; snowshoes; men carry loads with tumplines
138.....	Ganda	Fifty-foot canoes; paddles, no sails	Network of excellent roads; human porters
146.....	Aztecs	Dugout canoes	System of roads; stone, wood, and vine suspension bridges, litters; relays of couriers
150.....	Dahomeans	Crude dugouts	Loads carried by porters; hammock litters; couriers
226.....	Incas		Best roads ever built up to last century; causeways, culverts, ferries, suspension bridges; system of couriers; llamas
159.....	Mean		

* Source: George Peter Murdock, *Our Primitive Contemporaries* (New York, 1934).

† For a more detailed explanation of the method by which these ratings were derived see Hornell Hart and Donald L. Taylor, "Was There a Prehistoric Trend from Smaller to Larger Political Units?" *American Journal of Sociology*, XLIX (1944), 289–92.

better than even the Roman road system. Culverts, causeways, and bridges of wood, of stone, and of suspended vines were developed by these politically advanced preliterates. The Aztecs, the Dahomeans, and the Incas had organized systems of couriers to carry messages swiftly from one part of the empire to another.

As far, therefore, as one can judge from the study of modern preliterates, political development does seem to have been associated with relatively advanced methods of land transportation. But there appears to be a striking absence of any obvious connection between specific transportation inventions and political expansion. Neither sails on boats nor use of domesticated animals as beasts of burden or as steeds seem to have been closely associated with preliterate political expansion. The association between political development and transportation seems rather to have been merely one aspect of the association between governmental growth and general technological advancement.

ACCELERATION OF PREHISTORIC TECHNOLOGICAL AND POLITICAL DEVELOPMENT

When the modern preliterate peoples are arranged according to the degree of advancement in their technological culture, it is found that those with the simplest tools tend also to have the simplest governments, while those with relatively high technological developments tend to have the most highly developed governments.[3] Since this is true for contemporary tribes, it is reasonable to assume that the same relation held true for prehistoric peoples.

Peoples of exceedingly simple technological development, such as the Tasmanians, the Veddas, the Botucudos, the Fuegians, and the Australian Aranda, had approximately similar levels of political organization.[4] The following abstract describes the government of the Aranda: "The political, judicial, and military institutions of the Aranda were very rudimentary. Tribal government did not exist. The natives were divided into innumerable local groups, each made up of two or three families, a family consisting of a man, his wives, and children. Each had its recognized hunting grounds as well as the totem center about which its ceremonial life revolved. Only within these atomistic groups did anything resembling political organization

3. For a mathematical demonstration of this relationship see Hart and Taylor, *op. cit.*, pp. 290–96.

4. Julius E. Lips, "Government," in *General Anthropology*, ed. Franz Boas (Boston: D. C. Heath & Co., 1938), p. 491.

prevail. Each local group acknowledged the leadership of a totem chief, whose authority was vague, dependent upon his personal prestige, and mainly of a religious character. On all important matters the chief consulted with a council of the oldest and most respected men of the group. When a serious crime occurred, this council of elders organized parties to execute blood vengeance."[5]

The lower Old Stone Age technological level, whose governmental institutions corresponded roughly with that represented by the Australian Aranda, and by the other peoples just listed, prevailed in West Central Europe previous to about 100,000 B.C. The amount of territory held by any single government, in this Old Stone Age level of technological and political development, seems likely to have been approximately of the same order in size as the amount controlled by single political units among aboriginal Australians. This was about four thousand to ten thousand square miles, according to Lips.[6]

The Neolithic, or New Stone Age, with pottery, domesticated animals, loom weaving, and stone tools sharpened by grinding, prevailed in West Central Europe about 5000 B.C. The modern primitive peoples whose technology and governmental development have best typified this level of cultural evolution are the Hopi, inhabiting six pueblo villages in Arizona.

Politically, each pueblo village was independent; there was neither a federal government nor a supreme chief. A village was made up of a number of clans, each consisting of a group of families united by descent in the female line. The clans owned the cultivated land. Authority over the village was vested in a council of hereditary clan chiefs. Certain members of the council held special offices. The village chief directed all communal activities and exercised a right of veto over all proposals coming before the council. A war chief held the military command and also acted as police officer, with power to stop quarrels, using force if necessary. The council exercised judicial as well as administrative and legislative functions, settling all disputes.

The fact that technology and government are not perfectly correlated is illustrated by comparing the Hopi with the Iroquois. Technologically the Iroquois were somewhat inferior to the Hopi, with an index only about two-thirds as great. The Hopi had acquired loom weaving, stone dishes, and domesticated turkeys, while the Iroquois

5. Abridged from George Peter Murdock, *Our Primitive Contemporaries* (1934), pp. 22–45.
6. *Op. cit.*, p. 491.

had none of these. But politically the Iroquois were far in advance of the Hopi, having an index more than twice as great. The Iroquois had developed a League of Nations. This league had a council which decided matters by a unanimous vote. Member-nations could go to war without the consent of the league if the war did not interfere with league interests. The Iroquois League was formed about A.D. 1570. When it was first known to white men, it was composed of five tribes and occupied the territory extending from the east watershed of Lake Champlain to the west watershed of the Genesee River, and from the Adirondacks southward to the territory of the Conestoga Indians, who lived on the Susquehanna River and its branches.[7] This territory covered approximately 22,500 square miles.

After the coming of the Dutch, from whom they acquired firearms, the Iroquois were able to extend their conquests until their dominion was acknowledged from the Ottawa River to the Tennessee, and from the Kennebec to the Illinois River and Lake Michigan—a territory approximating 560,000 square miles. This twenty-five-fold increase illustrates once more the relationship between technology and political power. Given a political organization which has the culture patterns necessary for establishing government on a fairly complex level, the addition of a marked technological advantage (such as firearms) may increase a group's power of conquest many fold.

However, the rifle belonged to the machine age, not to the early Neolithic level on which the Iroquois lived before borrowing firearms from the Dutch. The territory of the five nations, therefore, with its approximately 22,500 square miles, represents the best evidence available as to the maximum geographical sway attained in the technological level which existed in Central Europe about 5000 B.C. and in Egypt about 10,000 B.C.

As we have seen above, the type of government associated with the Old Stone Age level of technology consisted of mere clans, made up of a few families and led by a chief who consulted with a council of elders. The type of government associated with the New Stone Age level of technology included at one extreme mere villages made up of clans, having a ruling council composed of clan chiefs; at the other extreme it included the five-nation Iroquois League. When technology developed to the point of working metals, political organization increased still further in complexity. An example is found in ancient Peru.

7. Frederick W. Hodge, *Handbook of American Indians North of Mexico*, Part I (Washington, D.C., 1907).

Technologically the Incas of Peru had advanced into the age of metals. Their smiths produced bronze knives, axes, chisels, hoes, spades, needles, and tweezers, as well as delicately wrought gold and silver jewelry. Their engineers constructed irrigation canals as much as sixty miles in length, with aqueducts to carry them over the valleys. They also built suspension bridges and constructed walls of huge blocks of stone so accurately fitted to each other (by grinding with wet sand) that a knife blade could not be inserted between them. They erected palaces having running water piped from hot and cold springs.

The political life of the Incas was built on the basis of clans, composed of ten families each. One hundred clans combined to form a tribe. Four tribes formed a province. The provinces were grouped into four "quarters," each ruled by a viceroy. These various political groupings were ruled over by a hierarchy of officials, spied upon by a corps of secret agents. At the apex of the pyramid stood the divine ruler, directing the operations of the vast administrative machinery with an authority not far from absolute. Under this ruler economic production, distribution, and consumption were regulated by state socialism.[8]

The Incas had no written language and thus belonged among the preliterate peoples. The Aztecs of ancient Mexico, however, had a picture-written language and had begun to carve historic dates on their monuments and public buildings, so that they must be regarded as over the threshold into written history.

The ancient Mexicans worked copper, silver, and gold with skill. They had developed an astronomy which estimated the length of the year more accurately than did that of the ancient Egyptians. Emerging out of an archaic Neolithic civilization, their little independent villages had grown into cities, with magnificent stone buildings, dominated by great temple pyramids, sometimes over a hundred feet in height, faced with sculptured masonry. One of these was the island city of Mexico, connected with the mainland by a number of long artificial causeways, pierced by sluices and protected by drawbridges. Over one of them a double aqueduct of stone and cement brought a constant supply of fresh water.

Politically, the Aztecs, like the Incas, had emerged into the empire-building stage. About A.D. 1400 Mexico City formed an offensive and defensive alliance with two other Aztec city-states, and soon the

8. Murdock, *op. cit.*, pp. 403–46.

three dominated a vast area. Their kings and nobles ruled over subject provinces, collecting regular tribute and maintaining large armies.[9]

The Incas and Aztecs were fairly comparable in technological and scientific achievement with the Egyptians of the Pyramid Age, about the thirtieth to the twenty-fifth century B.C., before horses were introduced. At that time Egypt and the Near East were in the Bronze and Iron Age, with hieroglyphic and cuneiform writing, a knowledge of astronomy which included an estimate of the length of the year as $365\frac{1}{4}$ days, preservation of grain and other foods, elaborate specialization of crafts, use of hewn stone, and the building of elaborately specialized buildings.

This level of technology, in the Old World, corresponded with a degree of political development under which the largest area ever ruled from any one capital was Sargon's Semitic empire, which reached its peak about 2400 B.C., and which ruled over approximately 250,000 square miles. This compares with an area of about 500,000 square miles held by the Aztec League and with the empire of approximately 600,000 square miles held by the Incas. In other words, both in the Old World and in the New, the dawn of history, with elaborate architecture, use of metals, and accurate astronomical measurement of the length of the year, coincided with the achievement of governments ruling over areas of from about a quarter- to a half-million square miles.

The growth of political organization up to the village level, in which several clans were banded together into an independent tribal unit, required hundreds of thousands of years of cultural evolution. But development from that stage to empires, such as grew up in both the Old World and the New during the early metal ages at the dawn of history, before the introduction of horse transportation, required only approximately 10,000 years. This shorter period of time embodied a far larger amount of political growth. During the roughly 95,000 years from 100,000 to 5500 B.C., *in West Central Europe*, the increase in maximum area controlled by any one government was in the general neighborhood of 15,000 square miles. During the 3,750 years from 5500 to 750 B.C. (when the Iron Age reached West Central Europe) the gain was in the general neighborhood of 600,000 square miles. For the earlier period the rate of gain was approximately 0.15

9. *Ibid.*, pp. 359–402; T. A. Joyce, *Mexican Archaeology* (London, 1914), pp. 109–33; Herbert J. Spinden, *Ancient Civilizations of Mexico and Central America* (New York, 1938), pp. 182–89.

square mile per year; during this later period it was approximately 150 square miles per year, or nearly a thousand times as great. Even more emphatically, therefore, this quantitative estimate confirms the conclusion that, in prehistoric times, areas controlled by any one government have been increasing with accelerating speed. The indicated acceleration is so great that fairly large errors might exist in the estimates of early areas and dates without altering the general conclusion. Furthermore, this accelerating political growth was closely related to accelerating advances in technology.

LAND-BORNE EMPIRE GROWTH IN THE AGE
OF HORSE TRANSPORTATION

The horse was introduced into Egypt by the Hyksos invaders, about 1700 B.C.[10] Horses had appeared in Babylonia about three hundred years earlier, and it seems probable that they were first domesticated in Central Asia.[11] Although potters' wheels had been used in Egypt before 3000 B.C., the wheeled vehicle seems to have been absent there until introduced along with the horse by the Hyksos. Four-wheeled wagons, drawn by asses and oxen, were in use in Mesopotamia about 3300 B.C. India had bullock carts about 3000 B.C.[12] Horse-drawn vehicles continued to be the most rapid and efficient means of land transportation in the Western world until the introduction of railroads.

The growth of land-borne empires in the Western world during the Horse Age is shown in Table 2; the corresponding facts for Asia are shown in Table 3; and both of these developments are shown graphically in Chart I. Any given point, on any terrace in Chart I, *A*, represents the largest land-borne area which, up to that date, had ever been ruled from a single capital in the Western world. Corresponding meanings apply to the points on the terraces in Chart I, *B*.

The curved lines running through these terraces represent logistic trends.[13] The essential characteristic of a logistic trend is that it rep-

10. James Henry Breasted, *Ancient Times* (New York, 1944), pp. 102–4.

11. *Encyclopaedia Britannica* (11th ed., 1929), II, 755a.

12. A. L. Kroeber, *Anthropology* (New York, 1923), pp. 430, 441, 448, 462, and Supplement, pp. 22 and 27.

13. The generalized mathematical formula for the logistic curve is given by the equation

$$Y_c = K_1 + \frac{K_2}{1 + 10^{g(d.5 - d_a)}}, \tag{1}$$

where d_a is any assigned date within the time limits for which the curve is valid, Y_c is the calculated value on the curve for that date, K_1 is the lower limit from which the curve arises, K_2 is the growth zone, K_1 plus K_2 is the upper limit toward which the curve approaches, g is the logarithm of growth, and $d_{.5}$ is the date at which the curve reaches half of its indicated growth and undergoes its inflection from acceleration to retardation.

resents a development which begins slowly, then speeds up, then slows down and stops. In a true logistic surge the slowing-down occurs at the reverse of the rates at which the development speeded up. In Chart I both trends have been largely in the speeding-up stage, but the Eastern world trend began to slow down about A.D. 500, as can be seen by close examination of the curve.

TABLE 2*

LAND-BORNE EMPIRES OF THE WESTERN WORLD WHICH BROKE PREVIOUS RECORDS IN AREAS WHICH THEY CONTROLLED FROM THE DAWN OF HISTORY TO THE PRESENT TIME, WITH DATES OF MAXIMUM POWER, NAMES OF CONQUERORS OR DOMINANT PEOPLES, AND ESTIMATED AREAS

Date	Dominant People	Conqueror†	Approximate Area (Square Miles)
2400 B.C.	Semitic	Sargon	249,000
1450 B.C.	Egyptian		690,000
600 B.C.	Median		940,000
500 B.C.	Persian	Darius	2,325,000
A.D. 750	Saracen		4,380,000
A.D. 1725	Russian	Peter the Great	5,860,000
A.D. 1800	Russian		7,490,000
A.D. 1944	Russian		8,490,000

* Source: Hornell Hart, "The Logistic Growth of Political Areas," *Social Forces*, XXVI (1948), 397.

† Table I omits two famous land-borne empires—Senacherib's Assyrian, which had approximately 581,000 square miles of territory in 700 B.C., and Alexander's Macedonian, which had approximately 2,610,000 square miles in 330 B.C. But it will be noted that the area of each of these empires had been exceeded by earlier governments. For the Roman Empire see p. 41.

TABLE 3*

LAND-BORNE EMPIRES OF ASIA WHICH BROKE PREVIOUS RECORDS IN AREAS WHICH THEY CONTROLLED, FROM THE DAWN OF HISTORY TO THE PRESENT TIME, WITH DATES OF MAXIMUM POWER, DYNASTIES, AND ESTIMATED AREAS

Date	Dynasty or Conqueror	Approximate Area (Square Miles)
1900 B.C.	Hsia Dynasty	52,000
1639 B.C.	Shang Dynasty	160,000
1300 B.C.	Shang Dynasty	307,000
800 B.C.	Chou Dynasty	398,000
500 B.C.	Chou Dynasty	680,000
225 B.C.	Tsin Dynasty	1,021,000
174 B.C.	Mao-Tun, the Hun	2,545,000
A.D. 100	Han Dynasty	2,690,000
A.D. 668	Tang Dynasty	4,750,000
A.D. 1290	Kublai and Genghis Kahn	9,208,000

* Source: *Ibid.*

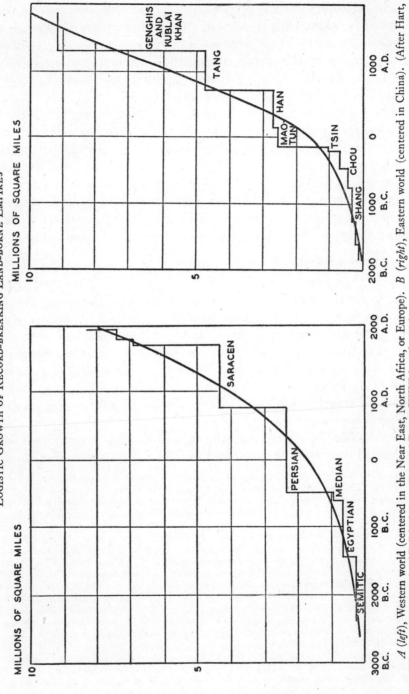

CHART I

LOGISTIC GROWTH OF RECORD-BREAKING LAND-BORNE EMPIRES

A (*left*), Western world (centered in the Near East, North Africa, or Europe). *B* (*right*), Eastern world (centered in China). (After Hart, "The Logistic Growth of Political Areas," *Social Forces*, XXVI [1948], 398.)

The reliability of these trends is discussed in the source from which Chart I is taken. On the basis of the evidence there presented, it is statistically established, beyond any reasonable doubt, that such empires grew acceleratingly during the thirty-five hundred years of the Horse Age in transportation (1700 B.C.–A.D. 1800) and that the trend has been of the general logistic type.[14]

The basic facts about the growth of political areas during the age of horse transportation may, then, be summarized by saying that the record-breaking empire areas, both in the Western and in the Eastern world, increased acceleratingly, along logistic trends, and that these increases were related to the introduction of wheeled vehicles and horses, harness, the building of road systems, the increasing mastery of bridge-building, the increasing length of ships, and the development of elaborate applications of manpower to rowing galleys.

DEEP-SEA SAILING AND THE GROWTH OF SEA-BORNE EMPIRES

The preceding section has dealt with land-borne political growth. But water transportation was developing during the same period. In ancient times navigators were unable to lay courses accurately for any great distance out of sight of land, so that most water travel was on rivers and along coastlines. Sails, rigging, and rudders were crude, and ships were unable to sail close into the wind. Ships were small and likely to spring leaks or go to pieces in storms. Under such conditions sea travel was definitely limited in scope, and ancient sea-borne empires were small.

In the Mediterranean area the earliest historic governments which extended their territory by major use of fleets were the Greek and the

---

14. That the above-described surge of growth in political areas was inaugurated by the use of the horse is suggested by Quincy Wright's comments made during the conference at which this paper was read. It may also be noted that, before the horse and the wheeled vehicle reached Egypt, the Near East, which had these transportational improvements first, held the record for empire size.

Hans Morgenthau raised the objection that the size of political units in the Western world went on growing (with fluctuations) throughout the Horse Age, in spite of the absence of any major improvements in the speed of land transportation between the time of Julius Caesar and Napoleon. Other transportational indexes, however, do reflect advances in transportational technology during these thirty-five hundred years. During the first two thousand years of the Horse Age, river and coastal transportation was being improved, as reflected in the increasing length of ships (Hornell Hart, *The Technique of Social Progress* [New York, 1931], p. 69), and in the improved application of manpower shown by development from about 700 B.C. onward, of biremes, triremes, and more complex forms of galley (Romola and R. C. Anderson, *The Sailing-Ship—Six Thousand Years of History* [London, 1926]). On land the growth of empires during the Horse Age was closely related to the development of road systems (*Encyclopaedia Britannica* [11th ed., 1929], XXII, 416–17). A more specific index of developing transportational technology during the last two thousand years of the Horse Age was the gradual lengthening of maximum bridge spans (Hart, *op. cit.*, p. 74).

Phoenecian, reaching areas of approximately 250,000 square miles each. The Roman Empire, with a land area of approximately 2,000,-000 square miles in A.D. 117, may be regarded as intermediate between the land-borne and the sea-borne types. It used fleets, but its major conquests were made by land armies.

In early modern times the Norsemen began to make sea-borne conquests. From 874 onward, Iceland and Greenland began to be opened up by Norway and Denmark. It was after the fringes of the New World had thus been penetrated by Europeans that a basic change in water transportation took place, between A.D. 1100 and 1500.

One of the factors in this change was the shift in major reliance from manpower to wind power in the driving of ships. In ancient times the great sea battles were fought in triremes and in more heavily oared galleys.[15] But oared ships reached the final stage of their development about 1500. When Henry V was building large vessels for his fleet in 1413, none of them seems to have been galleys. Of the 102 vessels in the Spanish Armada, in 1588, only 4 were galleys.[16] In the meantime, during the thirteenth century, two inventions had been made which were basic to the transformation of the Viking boat into the real sailing ship. One of these was the stern rudder; the other, the bowsprit. With these, and the deep-draught hull, ships were enabled to take full advantage of any wind.[17]

The second basic change in water transportation was the development of deep-sea navigation. A crucial invention was the mariner's compass, knowledge of which was diffusing in Europe during the period from 1100 to 1300. Other developments in navigation were also taking place. Tables of the stars, drawn up by Arzachel and by Alphonso X, were published in Spain in 1080 and in 1252, respectively; Chaucer translated an Arabic work about the astrolabe in 1391; Tamerlane founded an observatory at Samarkand, about 1420, and soon published revised tables of the stars; Henry (the Navigator) of Portugal made his voyages and investigations into deep-sea navigation between 1419 and 1460.[18]

The foregoing navigational developments occurred before the voyages of Columbus. Many major innovations (such as the invention of the sextant and of the chronometer) did not occur until later. Indeed, the major developments of modern navigation seem to have taken place *after* the discovery of the New World. Branch and Brock-Wil-

---

15. Anderson, *op. cit.*, pp. 39–44.   17. *Ibid.*, pp. 82–87, 114–15, and 135.
16. *Encyclopaedia Britannica*, XX, 508.   18. *Ibid.*, VI, 175–77; XVI, 172–73.

liams' *Short History of Navigation* (1942) mentions eighty-nine dates between 1200 and the present, of which eighty-four are after 1499. These dates cluster in two groups—one between 1500 and 1674; the other from 1675 to the present. Each of these surges can be fitted closely with a logistic trend, as indicated by curves *B* and *D* in Chart VI (p. 54).

Parallel with the above-mentioned developments in sailing vessels, and in navigation, political expansion into the New World took place. The North and South American continents were opened up by the Spanish, Portuguese, Dutch, French, and British. Of these early-modern sea-borne empires, the largest was the Spanish, which broke all records about 1763, with an area of approximately 5,400,000 square miles.[19]

From 1492 to 1763 the growth of the colonial areas in the New World was slow at first, then it accelerated, and, finally, when the desirable territories had more and more been taken possession of, it slowed down as it approached the limit of total occupation of the hemisphere. A logistic curve provides a convenient mathematical summary of this growth. The trend appears as curve *A* in Chart VI.

After the logistic growth of European colonies in the New World had reached about 95 per cent of its maximum, the territorial expansion of the United States began. This growth also conformed to a logistic trend, as presented graphically in Chart II and also by curve *G* in Chart VI.[20] The evidence, summarized by this curve, indicates that the surge of territorial growth which has occupied the entire life of this country up to the present is practically completed. Whether the United States will develop a second spurt of growth in area is an open question.

Later than the colonial expansion of Europe into America, but earlier by centuries than the growth of the United States, occurred the expansion of Russia. The best available estimates of Russia's area, in thousands of square miles, at the dates indicated, are as follows: 1490, 130; 1560, 1,680; 1725, 6,880; 1796, 7,490; 1886, 8,460; 1895, 8,640; 1900, 8,660; 1910, 8,650; 1914, 8,760; 1930, 8,140; 1935,

---

19. William R. Shepherd, *Historical Atlas* (1929), pp. 107–10, 128*b*–*c*, and 136.

20. While the exact mathematical form of the curve fitted to this growth is open to discussion, it is evident that a trend so regular as this would not occur by chance as often as once in millions of times. For this trend, the coefficient of curvilinear correlation ($\bar{\rho}^2$) is .942; N is 31; m is 4; F is 147, whereas the value of F which would occur by chance once in a thousand times is only 7.0 (see Frederick E. Croxton and Dudley J. Cowden, *Applied General Statistics* [New York, 1940], p. 878).

8,240; 1940, 8,350; and 1944, 8,490.[21] These data can be regarded only as approximations. However, a logistic trend fits them much more closely than can be explained by chance.[22] This trend is shown graphically in curve *C* of Chart VI. Since this was a land-borne development, it cannot be directly charged to navigational inventions. It was presumably accompanied by development of roads, but no close

CHART II

AREA OF THE UNITED STATES, WITH LOGISTIC TREND FITTED, 1790–1945

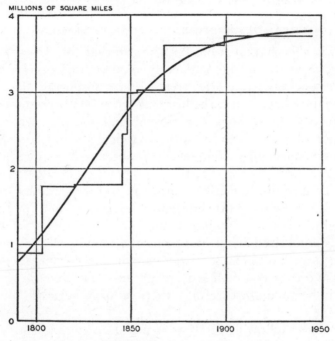

MILLIONS OF SQUARE MILES

Source: *Statistical Abstract of the United States*

relationship to any specific transportational invention has been discovered by the present writer.

The broad relationships between the growth of sea-borne empires and water-transportational technology, before the advent of the steamship, may be summarized as follows. Water transportation before 1400 was almost wholly confined to rivers and to coastal travel. Under these conditions the sea-borne empires of the Greeks and the Phoenecians were small, and sea transportation played a subordinate

21. George V. Vernadski, *A History of Russia* (New Haven, 1929), pp. 17, 84–85, and 451; *World Almanac, passim; Statesman's Yearbook, 1940*, pp. 193 and 198.
22. The corrected coefficient of curvilinear correlation is .993; the critical ratio (Z/σ_z) is 7.9.

part in the development of other empires. But with the advent of deep-sea navigation, and of the stern rudder, the bowsprit, and other prerequisites to effective tacking against the wind, the Western Hemisphere was opened up, the area of Spanish holdings broke all previous records of empire areas, the United States and other New World nations grew up, and the beginnings of the British Empire appeared. However, the largest developments in navigational inventions and discoveries occurred after rather than before the discovery of the Western Hemisphere.

THE STATISTICAL DESCRIPTION OF THE INDUSTRIAL REVOLUTION

Earlier in this chapter it has been shown that the growth of political areas, even in ancient and early modern times, conformed to logistic (or possibly Gompertz) trends. For transportational developments the data have (until the last two centuries) been too fragmentary to justify any elaborate statistical analysis. But, when the Industrial Revolution began to dawn, historical and statistical records had become sufficiently complete to make possible more searching types of analysis.

The fitting of mathematical curves to social trends has been explored inductively by many different investigators, and the literature on the subject is too voluminous, and involves too many aspects, to be even summarized here. However, the reader who is unfamiliar with that branch of social statistics cannot safely dismiss its findings with dogmatic or common-sense negations. The remainder of this chapter is based upon careful inductions from scientific studies in that field.[23]

Much of the following analysis is based on comparisons between logistic trends. Such comparisons are facilitated by reducing the trends to a percentage basis.[24] On such a percentage basis, the best available indexes relating to modern sail and steam transportation are summarized in Chart III. As indicated there, transportation

23. For summaries and bibliographies see Hornell Hart, "Logistic Social Trends," *American Journal of Sociology*, L (1945), 337–52, and "Depression, War, and Logistic Trends," *ibid.*, LII (1946), 112–22.

24. If the reader will refer back to equation (1) (n. 13), he will note that K_2 represents the "growth zone"—i.e., the amount which the logistic curve rises from its base line to its maximum limit, measured in millions of square miles, or thousands of tons of shipping cleared, or billions of revenue passenger miles carried, or whatever units may be involved in the original series. In order to reduce a logistic to a percentage basis, K_2 is made to equal 100. In percentage terms the generalized formula for the logistic curve thus becomes

$$Y_c - K_1 = \frac{100}{1 + 10^{g\,(d.s - d_a)}}. \tag{2}$$

CHART III

SAIL AND STEAM TRANSPORTATION INDEXES: PERCENTAGE LOGISTICS, 1750–1930

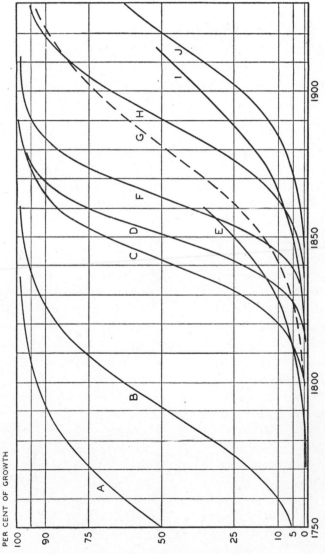

KEY TO CHART

A. Contributions to Navigation II

B. British Patents I

C. Locomotive Speeds

D. Sailing Tonnage: French Ports

E. Sailing Tonnage: World

F. Railway Track Added

G. Steam Power in Factories

H. Railway Track: World

I. Ship Tonnage Cleared: United Kingdom

J. World Steamship Tonnage

Sources of data, by letters: *A*, W. J. V. Branch and E. Brook-Williams, *A Short History of Navigation* (1942); *B*, Pitirim Sorokin, *Social and Cultural Dynamics* (1937), II, 164; *C*, Hornell Hart, "Technological Acceleration and the Atomic Bomb," *American Sociological Review*, XI (1946), 284; *D*, *Encyclopaedia Britannica* (11th ed.; 1929), XX, 549; *E*, Simon S. Kuznets, *Secular Movements in Production and Prices* (1930), p. 530; *F*, *ibid.*, pp. 526–27; *G*, see text; *H*, *Lincoln Library* (1941); Michael G. Mulhall, *Dictionary of Statistics* (1899); Augustus D. Webb, *New Dictionary of Statistics* (1911); *I*, Kuznets, *op. cit.*, pp. 426–28; *J*, same as *E*.

trends have generally conformed closely to logistic curves. Taking these trend lines in the order in which they crossed the 25 per cent level, the following comments are pertinent.

Curve *A* represents the second of the two modern spurts in the development of navigational theory, as explained on page 42.

Curve *B* represents the first of two surges in British patents. Among the patents whose granting helped to make up this surge were Watt's on the steam engine, Symington's and Fulton's on the steamboat, and Trevithick's on the first steam train running on a track—all these being granted between 1765 and 1810. This surge may be regarded as the growth of the basic ideas underlying the Steam Age aspect of the Industrial Revolution.

The process of practical improvement in railroad engines is reflected in curve *C*, representing speed records of locomotives.

Curve *D* represents the tonnage of sailing ships cleared through the ports of France. The logistic was fitted by Kuznets.

Curve *E* represents the trend of sailing-ship tonnage for the world as a whole. This trend line stops at 1860, because after that date the tonnage of sailing shipping in the world reversed its trend and thereafter followed a descending logistic. Similarly, as Kuznets has shown, the tonnage of sailing ships cleared through French ports (curve *D*) followed a descending logistic after 1870.

The *F* trend represents the surge of development in the rail network, as reflected in the logistic growth in miles of track added.

Curve *G* is an average of eleven mining, manufacturing, and commercial logistic trends, most of which were fitted originally by Kuznets. All these trends reached 1 per cent of their theoretical total growth between 1777 and 1813—i.e., after the applied phase of the Industrial Revolution had begun but before the rise of any of the series specifically reflecting steam transportation. The method of deriving this average curve will be discussed later.

The *H* trend represents total mileage of railway track in use in the world, as distinct from miles of new track added.

Curve *I* depicts the trend of ship tonnages cleared through the ports of the United Kingdom, as fitted by Kuznets. During the ninety-nine years from 1815 to 1913, the largest departure from the trend (in percentages) was less than 2.58 standard errors. But, from 1915 to 1921, shipping clearances dropped, remaining from 3 to 7 standard errors below, and never since then has the index gotten back to its old trend.

The final trend in Chart III—curve $\mathcal{J}$—represents the logistic growth of the total registered steamship tonnage of the world.

The expansion of electric-motor and internal-combustion-engine transportation formed a distinct development subsequent to that of steam transportation. Chart IV presents some of the major surges in this field. It should be noted that the time scale in Chart IV is three times as extended as that in Chart III. This is necessary in order to show clearly the slopes of these recent trends, which are much steeper than those in Chart III. The meaning of the individual trend lines of Chart IV may be epitomized as follows.

Curve A represents the trend of successive world speed records for nonstreamlined automobiles.

Curve B shows the trend in the number of revenue passengers carried on electric railways in the United States.

The C curve depicts the trend in the cumulative number of automobile patents, per million of population, in the United States. The logistic was fitted by Dr. Alice Davis.

Curve D represents motor-vehicle registrations, per 100 of population, in the United States. This logistic also was fitted by Dr. Davis.

The E trend represents successive world speed records for gas-engine airplanes, whether taking off from land or from sea. The jet plane appears at present to be starting a new speed series, not conforming to this logistic. It will be noted that curve E had a 5 per cent level as early as 1900, though the Wright brothers first flew in 1903. This is because, although the first flights were at an air speed of a little over thirty miles per hour, a logistic curve starting from zero fits better than one starting with K_1 equal to 30. Moreover, this is logical, since the successful flights by the Wright brothers were the outgrowth of many preliminary trials, corresponding to slower speeds on the theoretical curve.

The F curve represents the trend of successive world records of nonstop distance for planes.

Curve G represents the trend of Diesel-motor ship tonnage for the world.

When the facts summarized by Charts III and IV are taken together, certain basic principles of social change, as related to transportational inventions, become evident. Suppose we ask the question: "What was the effect of the invention of steam transportation upon the growth of political areas?" To have any scientific meaning, the phrase "invention of steam transportation" must be defined, in

CHART IV

ELECTRIC AND GASOLINE TRANSPORTATION INDEXES: PERCENTAGE LOGISTICS, 1890–1940

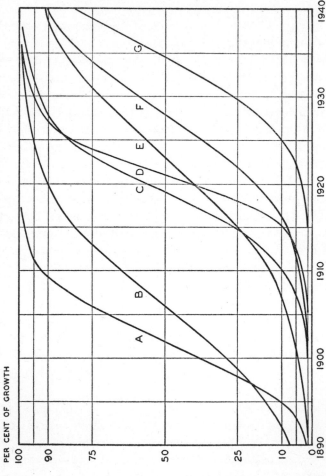

KEY TO CHART

A. Automobile Speeds

B. Electric Railway Revenue
   Passenger Miles

C. Cumulative Auto Patents

D. Motor Vehicle Registrations:
   United States

E. Airplane Speeds

F. Airplane Ranges

G. Motor-Ship Tonnage: World

Sources of data: *A*, Hornell Hart, "Technological Acceleration and the Atomic Bomb," *American Sociological Review*, XI (1946), 284; *B, Statistical Abstract of the United States; C*, Alice Davis, "Technicways in American Civilization," *Social Forces*, XVIII (1940), 317–30; *D, ibid.; E*, same as *A; F*, Hornell Hart, "Logistic Social Trends," *American Journal of Sociology*, L (1945), 341; *G*, same as *D* in Chart I.

terms which would enable us to classify this with a series of other transportational inventions, so as to develop useful generalizations for prediction and control. Watt took out his first patent on his steam engine in 1769. It was thirty-four years later that the logistic surge associated with applications of steam power in factories reached 1 per cent of its theoretical growth (see curve *G* of Chart III). The first steamboats, and Trevithick's patent for a steam train on a track, came during the first decade after 1800. But world railway mileage and world steamship tonnage did not reach 1 per cent of their logistic growth until 1834 and 1845, respectively. How, then, can the effects of steam transportation be disentangled from the effects of steam power as applied to manufacturing?

Moreover, Watt's invention was no isolated phenomenon. Others before him had been working at the problem of steam pumps.[25] His patents were items in a great upsurge of inventions, the number of which, in successive ten-year periods, conforms to a logistic curve far more closely than can be explained by random fluctuation. This logistic upsurge of inventions had been preceded, more than a century earlier, by an upsurge in contributions to mathematics, which reached 1 per cent of its logistic growth in 1568.

Similar difficulties arise if one attempts to identify the "invention" of the electric railway, of the automobile, or of the airplane. Each of these has been an inextricable part of the vast upsurge in technology which has followed upon the steam phases of the Industrial Revolution. One may speculate upon this or that subordinate relation between each of these inventions and contemporary political growth. Yet the overtoweringly important fact would seem to be the underlying technological acceleration.

But suppose that the invention of the wheeled vehicle, and the domestication of the horse, the invention of deep-sea navigation, the locomotive, the steamship, the electric railway, the automobile, and the airplane could each be satisfactorily isolated as a unit, whose relations to political growth were to be analyzed scientifically. One notes that the Horse Transportation Age lasted thirty-five hundred years, the Deep-Sea Sailing Age about three hundred years, the Steam Transportation Age (throwing in the electric-railway phase) about seventy-five years, and the Gasoline Engine Age about thirty, with Diesels, jets, and prospective atomic-propulsion succeeding each other too rapidly to justify assigning any time periods as their

25. Abbott P. Usher, *A History of Mechanical Inventions* (New York, 1929), pp. 13–14.

"ages." What generalizations can be built up, about all those individual transportation inventions, which will be equally valid for the Horse Age and the Jet Propulsion Age?[26]

The present writer submits the following tentative propositions, as providing at least a promising basis of procedure for research in this field:

1. Where it can be shown that logistic, Gompertz, loglog, or other mathematically describable surges are more regular than can be explained by chance fluctuations, and fit significantly more closely than any alternative trend which has been suggested and tested, it is proposed that such a trend be regarded, at least tentatively, as the description of a unit phenomenon in social change.

2. Where such a trend has been fitted, but the data are insufficient to eliminate the possibility of chance, it is suggested that the reasonableness of the hypothetical trend be tested in the light of available and pertinent knowledge and that the curve be employed, in so far as it proves useful, as a tentative description of the phenomena which it summarizes. An example is the growth of colonial holdings by European powers in the Western Hemisphere from 1492 to 1776.

3. Where a series of related logistic surges are found to have developed during a given period of time (as was the case for various subdivisions of the Industrial Revolution), it is suggested that such logistics be averaged in order to arrive at general trend line, summarizing them all.[27]

26. Something of the confusion which may arise from ignoring the underlying facts of technological acceleration is suggested by the following remark, made by Mr. Brodie at the Institute meeting at which this paper was read: "I would venture to guess, for example, in terms of the whole economy of our civilization the change from transport on human foot to transportation on the horse's foot was more significant than the shift from the railroad to the airplane, even though in terms of the speeds involved the latter is much more drastic." To dismiss as negligible such basic differences as those between the Horse Age and the Air Age would seem to the present writer to exclude arbitrarily some of the most fundamental generalizations which emerge from scientific study of social change. But if no really fundamental, trustworthy, and useful generalizations can be arrived at by treating individual transportation inventions as isolated phenomena, how can any more comprehensive units of discourse be arrived at?

27. Such an average may be obtained by the following method. Every logistic curve had a date of inflection $(d_{.5})$ and a growth logarithm (g). Every such curve reaches 1 per cent of its theoretical growth at a date $(d_{.01})$ which is always $1.996/g$ time units before its date of inflection. Thus the logistic trend of world steamship tonnages reached its point of inflection in 1921, and had a growth logarithm of .02614. Dividing 1.996 by this g-value gives approximately 76 years as the time interval between $d_{.01}$ and $d_{.5}$ on this curve, which means that the logistic trend of steamship tonnages reached 1 per cent of its growth in 1845. Any closely related series of logistic trends can be combined by averaging their $d_{.01}$'s and their $d_{.5}$'s. A representative g for the combined series can then be found by taking the difference between these two average dates and dividing 1.996 by that difference. For example, the mean $d_{.5}$ for the eleven series represented by curve G in Chart III is 1881.7; the mean $d_{.01}$ is 1797.7; the difference is 84.0 years; and dividing 1.996 by 84.0 gives .02376 as the value of g for the combined series.

4. Wherever social trends are logistic in character, they can be compared by analyzing the relationships between their dates and their slopes. This procedure will be used in the next section in studying relationships between the transportational and political-area developments of the modern period.

5. Predictions cannot safely be made by mere extrapolation, but very useful predictions can be made if factors underlying the genesis, the termination, and the combination of given logistic trends are understood and applied intelligently.

POLITICAL GROWTH DURING THE STEAM TRANSPORTATION AGE

At first sight it seems to have been true that European expansion into the New World occurred during the age of deep-sea sailing, while acquisition of territory in Africa, Asia, and Oceania took place chiefly during the age of steamships. In order to explore this hypothesis further, an intensive study has been made of the growth of the British Empire.[28]

The best available data are indicated by the small circles in Chart V. These represent the total areas held by the British, at the indicated dates, out of the territories which were part of the Empire and Commonwealth in 1940. The heavy curve represents the over-all logistic trend from 1670 to 1940, around which the coefficient of curvilinear correlation is $\bar{\rho} = .993$.[29] This over-all logistic appears as curve I in Chart VI.

This long-run trend, however, does not fully describe the data. It will be observed in Chart V that, between 1788 and 1870 and again between 1875 and 1896, the departures of the data from the main

---

28. Data as to the areas of British holdings in recent years can be found in the *Statesman's Yearbook* and in various other sources. But the present writer has been able to locate only two comprehensive attempts to summarize the dates at which various parts of the British Empire and Commonwealth were acquired. One of these appeared in the *Encyclopaedia Britannica* (1910 ed.), IV, 608–9, and has been reprinted in subsequent editions in articles on "British Empire." The other appeared in the *World Almanac, 1916*, p. 451. From these two sources the dates of acquisition were determined for the various parts of the British holdings as they stood in 1940. The American colonies (which had an area of approximately 890,000 square miles in 1776) were not included, nor were the minor territories which the British acquired temporarily and lost. When areas were acquired gradually (e.g., in the case of Burma and of various parts of India), estimated interpolations were used.

29. The dotted line in Chart V represents a rectilinear trend, fitted by the least-squares criterion. The coefficient of correlation is $\bar{r} = .972$. The superiority of the logistic fit over the straight line would not occur by chance as often as once in six thousand times. For the straight line, Z is 2.140; for the logistic it is 3.880. The critical ratio of the difference is over 3.7. It will be noted that the gradual growth which occurred before 1669 did not conform to the over-all logistic trend. The sudden rise in 1669 was the acquisition of the Northwest Territories of Canada, under royal charter of the Hudson's Bay Company.

trend are in the form of smaller logistic surges. In the first of these subsurges, from 1788 to 1870, Britain acquired 4,370,000 square miles, including 70 per cent of her Australasian Dominion, approximately one-third of her holdings in India, and 70 per cent of her other territories in Asia. This subsurge in British growth is represented in Chart VI by curve *H*.

CHART V

TERRITORIAL GROWTH OF THE BRITISH EMPIRE, 1600–1940, WITH MAJOR AND MINOR LOGISTIC TRENDS

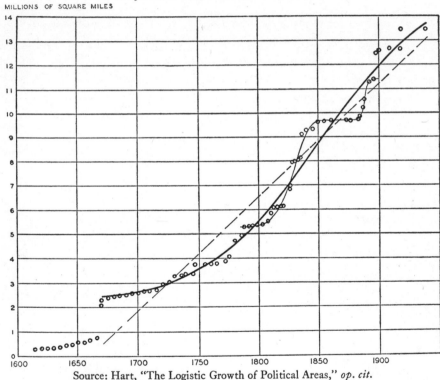

Source: Hart, "The Logistic Growth of Political Areas," *op. cit.*

The second sublogistic, between 1875 and 1896, accounts for 70 per cent of British holdings in Africa. This surge added 1,700,000 square miles to British area. It is represented by curve *L* in Chart VI. These two logistic curves fit far more closely than a straight-line trend for the two periods combined. Indeed, the superiority of the logistics would not have occurred by chance as often as once in ten million times.[30]

30. The curvilinear correlation ratio around the two sublogistics (deducting eight degrees of freedom for the four constants of each of the two curves) is .996, as compared with .958 for the rectilinear trend. The critical ratio of the *Z* difference is 5.6.

The midpoint in the African surge of British expansion came in 1888. This was followed by a sudden expansion in the colonial holdings of other European nations. The total areas controlled by five countries in 1890 and 1895 were as shown in Table 4. France's territorial gain was greater than that of the British. All together, the five empires listed in the table more than trebled their areas during these five years.

The foregoing indexes of political growth have been in terms of territorial expansion. Quite possibly the future development of gov-

TABLE 4*

TOTAL AREAS CONTROLLED BY FIVE COUNTRIES
1890 AND 1895

COUNTRY	HOLDINGS (THOUSANDS OF SQUARE MILES)	
	1890	1895
France........	1,132	3,093
Germany......	211	1,033
Portugal.......	241	952
Italy..........	111	426
Spain.........	362	603
Total.......	2,057	6,107

* Source: *World Almanac, 1891*, p. 232, and *Word Almanac, 1896*, p. 341.

ernmental power needs to be measured in terms of penetration rather than mere area. No reliable index of penetration is yet available, but future research might well be directed toward developing such an index.

TRANSPORTATION DEVELOPMENTS AND MODERN POLITICAL GROWTH

The two preceding sections have presented the available evidence, first, as to modern developments in transportation technology and, second, as to the growth of political areas. The present section brings these two types of evidence together. Graphically, this is done in Chart VI. The trends which represent expansion in political areas are drawn with solid lines; those which represent growth in transportational activities are depicted by lines drawn with dashes; those representing surges in the intellectual groundwork for transportational developments are depicted by dots. Of the area trends, curves *A*, *C*, and *G* have already been discussed. The growth of the United States

CHART VI

INDEXES OF POLITICAL GROWTH RELATED TO INDEXES OF TRANSPORTATIONAL DEVELOPMENT
PERCENTAGE LOGISTICS, 1500–1950

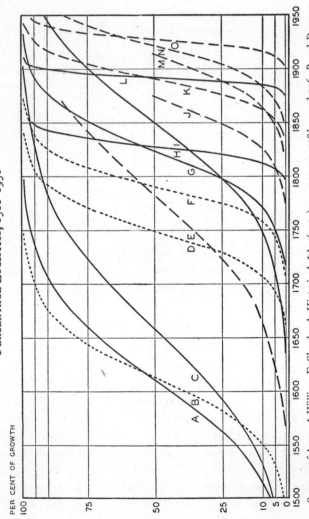

KEY TO CHART

A. Colonial Expansion: New World
B. Navigation I
C. Area of Russia
D. Navigation II
E. Tonnage: British Navy
F. British Patents I
G. United States Area
H. British Expansion: Australasia
I. British Empire Area
J. Sailing Tonnage: World
K. Railway Track: World
L. British Expansion: Africa
M. United Kingdom Ship Clearances
N. World Steamship Tonnage
O. Airplane Ranges

Sources of data: *A*, William F. Shepherd, *Historical Atlas* (1929), pp. 107–10, 128*b*–*c*, and 136; *B* and *D*, same as *A* in Chart III; *C*, Georgi V. Verdanshi, *A History of Russia* (1929), pp. 17, 84–85, and 451; *World Almanac*, *passim*; *Statesman's Yearbook*, *1940*, pp. 193 and 198; *E*, Mulhall, *op. cit.*, p. 415; Quincy Wright, *A Study of War* (1942), I, 670; letter from Secretary of the British Admiralty, dated July 30, 1947; *F*, same as *B* in Chart III; *G*, Chart II; *H*, *I*, and *L*, *Statesman's Yearbook*, *1939*, pp. xvi–xvii; *Encyclopaedia Britannica* (1938), IV, 177–78; *World Almanac*, *1916*, p. 451; *J*, same as *E* in Chart III; *K*, *M*, and *N*, same as *H*, *I*, and *J* in Chart III; *O*, same as *F* in Chart IV.

(curve G) and of the British Empire as a whole (curve H) reached their 25 per cent points fifty years before any of the transportational developments associated with the Industrial Revolution. The logistic growth of the British navy (curve E), which provides a reliable and valid index of certain aspects of English power, seems to have been related to the major geopolitical configuration centering around the development of the New World and can be regarded as a result of transportational invention only in the sense that the opening-up of the Western Hemisphere was a result of the development of deep-sea navigation.

British expansion in Australasia (curve H) conformed to a logistic trend which reached 1 per cent of its growth seventeen years later than the logistic trend of world sailing tonnage. But this outreach into the Pacific was, again, only an early and particularly swift phase of the commercial expansion precipitated by the Industrial Revolution. This is one of the several instances in which political growth appears to have taken place much more rapidly than the economic and technological developments with which it is associated. British expansion in Africa (curve L) started up thirty-two years after the logistic surge of world steamship tonnage reached its 1 per cent growth point, and again this political development was swifter than the accompanying commercial developments.

Curves K, M, N, and O in Chart VI represent major commercial logistic surges. The notable thing about them is that they were certainly subsequent to the major territorial expansions of the great nations.[31]

The evidence of Chart VI relative to the relationships between transportational developments and political growth may be summarized as follows. Political expansion into the Western Hemisphere seems to have been released by two centuries of preceding development of deep-sea navigation, a central instrument of which was the mariner's compass. The growth of the British navy, and the subse-

31. In rejoinder, it might be pointed out that world steamship tonnages did not reach 1 per cent of their logistic growth until 1845. But the British had acquired 90 per cent of their Far Eastern holdings by 1843. In connection with the foregoing analysis, the following remarks by Mr. Brodie should be considered: "One can make a very strong case for the steamship being responsible for the great revitalization of imperialist interests in the Far East for this reason: The Red Sea was, of course, always a very difficult area to sail ships; therefore, the Suez Canal would not have made much sense before the age of the steamship; then you had the whole monsoon area of the Indian Ocean to cross, and in the western Pacific you had belts of calms, and it does as a matter of simply historical chronology follow that there was a tremendous development of interest and acquisition of colonies in the Far East following the advent of the steam warship [sic]."

quent territorial expansion of the British Empire, seem to have been stimulated by the opening of the New World. The development of navigational theory and instruments was a parallel resultant, not a primary cause. The transportational developments in the ages of steam and gasoline were outgrowths of a surge of inventions which occurred a century earlier. British and American political growth occurred after the inventive surge but before those inventions had been extensively commercialized.

CONCLUSIONS

In the light of the evidence summarized in this chapter, it is now possible to draw some tentative conclusions in answer to the questions formulated at its beginning.

1. Individual transportational inventions and discoveries, such as the invention of the wheeled vehicle, the domestication of the horse, the development of deep-sea navigation, and the invention of the locomotive, the steamship, the electric car, the automobile, the gas-engine airplane, and the jet plane, have undoubtedly been related in significant ways to the expansion of political areas. The application of atomic power to transportation may be expected to have significant bearings upon the future development of world law and order. But to place major dependence upon the prediction or the control of political developments by means of analysis or control of transportational inventions is unwise. Even if the term "transportational invention and discovery" could be verifiably defined, so that all competent investigators could agree upon when such an event occurs, the number of identifiable examples is so small, and the related phenomena for the early examples are so difficult to measure adequately, that reliable scientific generalizations could not be built up. The common-sense pointing-out of relationships is intriguing, but it leaves the door wide open to subjective biases.

2. Transportational inventions and discoveries are inextricably part of much more inclusive cultural developments. Wheels were used for making pottery, for spinning, and for stationary machinery, as well as for vehicles; domestication of horses was closely related to domestication of other animals; the locomotive was part of the general steam-power revolution—and the like. Attempts to generalize about transportational inventions as though they were isolated are very likely to be delusory. Far more significant and useful results can be obtained by more fundamental scientific analyses of cultural

change in its more inclusive aspects. While prediction from or about individual transportational inventions is very difficult and unreliable, the prediction of general technological and other cultural trends has been demonstrated to be practicable and could undoubtedly be vastly improved if competently trained and adequately aided minds were to devote sufficient attention to it. Instead of waiting until mechanical inventions have produced cultural-lag crises, an adequate understanding of the basic principles of social change should make it possible to predict future developments accurately enough to adjust to them in advance. Pioneering advances in this direction have already been made in Ogburn's *The Social Effects of Aviation* (1946). If it were impossible to at least begin working out adjustments to technological changes before these changes occurred, the future of civilization would be dark indeed, for the accelerating destructiveness and swiftness of atomic V-bombs (and the like) leave less and less time for any adaptive experiments.

3. The fitting of logistic and other mathematical trend lines to various aspects of social change has now been carried far enough, by enough different investigators, to establish the statistical significance and validity of many such trends. In the published work of these investigators, various preliminary generalizations have been developed which have prima facie bearings of major significance in relation to technology and international relations.

4. In the absence of any adequate science of social change, it is not possible, as yet, to reach any trustworthy conclusion as to whether the recent swift acceleration of technological change will force the development of international controls adequate enough to prevent the destruction of civilization.

5. The answer to the fifth question formulated at the beginning of this chapter is beyond the assignment of the present author. But he asks permission to close with the expression of his belief that no plan for meeting the atomic crisis looks at all hopeful unless it includes the most promising attainable steps for developing a real social science, utilizing the best available resources toward discovering operationally adequate programs.

THE STEAM AND STEEL COMPLEX AND INTERNATIONAL RELATIONS

By Abbott Payson Usher

INVENTIONS OF PEACE AND WAR AND INTERNATIONAL AFFAIRS

INTERNATIONAL relations are affected by two classes of technological change: broad changes affecting the world economy as a whole and specific changes in the technology of warfare. New economic and social tensions are created by the disturbance of interregional relationships as a result of changes in the character and intensity of economic activity in politically important regions. Changes in economic importance result in changes in political prestige and influence which may lead to war. These underlying economic dislocations develop slowly as a result of positive and comprehensive transformations of the entire economic life and structure of the individual region and its neighboring regions. International complications are an end result of a long sequence of convergent technical developments operating over long periods of time.

Analysis of the influence of technology upon international relations thus requires full and explicit recognition of the organic character of the process of innovation. Individual items of invention and discovery are submerged in a broad process of cumulative synthesis. The impact of the Industrial Revolution upon international relations was not significantly revealed until the last decades of the nineteenth century—after a century and a half had elapsed since the basic inventions in power engineering and ironmaking. The consequences of these technical developments are still incompletely revealed. Technical skills are imperfectly diffused, and many important resources are not utilized.

The development of new technologies in warfare presents special problems in timing. Many applications are dependent upon a mature industrial community, so that military inventions do not enter into effective use more rapidly than inventions for peacetime activity. The development of all ordnance during the eighteenth and nineteenth centuries was dominated by technical difficulties in manufacture. At the present time, however, the military applications of aviation and atomic fission are proceeding more rapidly than any associated applications to general economic activity. Military technology becomes an independent source of international disturbance and tension.

The present crisis in international relations is primarily due to disturbances in the balance of power growing out of the Industrial Revolution of the eighteenth and nineteenth centuries. It is painfully intensified by developments in warfare that rest upon technical innovations that will not be fully exploited in the community as a whole in less than a century or a century and a half. We experience the consequences of two centuries of positive accomplishment simultaneously with all the difficulties of adjustment to changes whose ultimate consequences we cannot possibly foresee.

TRANSFORMATION OF THE WORLD ECONOMY BY THE INDUSTRIAL REVOLUTION

The Industrial Revolution was the culmination of a long sequence of inventions directed toward the comprehensive application of mechanical energy to industry, transport, and agriculture. Prime movers and operative mechanisms ultimately came to be made largely of iron and steel. The energy economy was thus closely identified with steam and steel. Water power was an important supplement, and, in agriculture and transport, animal power was important until the generalization of the internal combustion engine.

The development of an economy based primarily upon the use of mechanical energy gave an entirely new complexion to the world economy. The older economy was dominated by food supplies and by the great differences between the costs of transport by water and on land. The massing of population and of economic activity was a function of the geography of food production and of maritime and inland water transport.[1]

This older economy was essentially a maritime economy. It consisted effectively of the maritime fringe of the continents. Full command of oceanic navigation made it a global economy in a somewhat restricted sense of the word, but there were vast continental interiors that were wholly isolated and undeveloped. Although the new technology, based on fully generalized use of power, was ultimately destined to open up all the deep continental interiors, the leadership of Great Britain in the new industrial development made the new tech-

---

1. William H. Dean, Jr., *The Theory of the Geographic Location of Economic Activities* (Cambridge, Mass.: Harvard University Press, 1938), pp. 24–33.

niques an added source of strength to Great Britain and to her position as the outstanding sea power in a maritime world.

In the sixteenth and seventeenth centuries there was a sharp contest for control of the high seas between the northern sea powers and the peninsular powers. In the eighteenth century France and Great Britain were left as outstanding contenders for supremacy. The establishment of acknowledged spheres of influence preceded the major developments of the technology based on steam and steel. The problems of imperialism and of world politics were complicated by the ambitions of France in Europe, so that there were two zones of diplomatic tension and military conflict. The problems in Europe and emphasis upon nationalism obscure the effective importance of imperialism and the world economy.

The maritime world economy persisted as a dominant feature until about 1880. The most concrete basis for dating the passing of the older economy is afforded by the beginning of the agricultural depression, whose onset was so sharply marked in Great Britain by the year 1878. This date line is highly significant because it marks the massive entrance into the world market of the great interior regions specializing in cereal production. There had been an international grain trade of restricted importance for many years, but costs of imported grains were high and imports were specifically supplemental to home-grown grain in Britain and in northern and Mediterranean Europe. The novel picture of the period of the "depression" lay in the combination of massive imports with costs that menaced the local grain-growers in northern Europe. There remained only the choice between contraction of cereal acreage or protection. Britain, Denmark, and Holland accepted the necessity of restriction of cereal culture; France and Germany took refuge in protection.

This development of the grain trade was a conspicuous and commanding demonstration of the emergence of rail transport as a primary factor in the world economy. It marks the establishment of a rail network of sufficient compass in the United States and in Europe fully to disclose the possibility of opening all the great continental masses to world trade. The progressive mechanization of agriculture was also creating the possibility of full utilization of great regions at the margins of arable culture, too dry for general farming but well adapted to specialized culture of the small grains. This development completed the pattern of regional specialization initiated by the development of heavy-industry centers. The provision of railroads and iron ships was a basic feature of the development of demand for heavy industrial products, and the cheap food provided by the specialized agricultural areas made it possible to concentrate population in the great industrial areas of northern Europe and northeastern United States.

THE ENERGY ECONOMY

The distinctive features of the energy economy lie in the mechanization of industry, transportation, and agriculture. Industry in this new economy tends toward concentration around primary sources of energy or at urban sites of major accessibility. The outstanding urban sites are the great seaports which serve as contact points between large networks of inland transport and oceanic navigation.[2]

The great metropolitan areas are thus sites which have both commercial and industrial functions. They are centers of wholesale trade and distribution as well as centers of manufacture. These functions involve also important concentrations of banking and other financial activities, so that the "money" market becomes the most explicit symbol of the intensity and scope of the economic influence of the urban area. In many instances the primary economic sites are also used for civil and ecclesiastical administration, so that the entire range of urban functions is very broad. These urban functions are not in themselves distinctive of the energy economy, but the scale of concentration has increased markedly as a result of the scope of the network of inland transport developed under the influence of a comprehensive application of mechanical power.[3] Full analysis of urban concentration serves to emphasize the profound importance of the technology of transport. Although the basic inventions are closely associated with the technical development of power engineering in industry, many aspects of the transformation of the transport system are sufficiently independent to require separate treatment.

2. The analysis of this economy is developed by H. J. Mackinder, *Britain and the British Seas* (New York, 1902); P. Vidal de la Blache, *Tableau de la géographie de la France* (Paris, 1911); E. Lavisse, *Histoire de France* (Boston, 1919); Alfred Weber, *Über den Standort der Industrien*, Vol. I: *Reine Theorie des Standorts der Industrien* (Tübingen, 1909), translated by C. J. Friedrich as *Theory of the Location of Industries* (Chicago, 1928); T. Palander, *Beiträge zur Standorts Theorie* (Upsala, 1935); Edgar M. Hoover, *Location Theory and the Shoe and Leather Industries* (Cambridge, Mass., 1937), and *The Location of Economic Activity* (New York: McGraw-Hill Book Co., 1948).

3. Felix Auerbach, "Das Gesetz der Bevolkerungskonzentration," *Petermann's Mittheilungen*, 1913, pp. 74–75; G. K. Zipf, *National Unity and Disunity* (Bloomington, 1941), and "The Unity of Nature: Least-Action and Natural Social Science," *Sociometry*, V (1942), 53–58; John Q. Stewart, "Concerning 'Social Physics,'" *Scientific American*, CLXXVIII (May, 1948), 20–23.

The energy economy made possible a great increase in both the mass of the population and its concentration. The food-oriented economy of medieval and modern Europe produced a population pattern that reached limiting densities at levels of 125 persons per square mile when relatively large areas were averaged. Europe was gradually becoming maturely settled at density levels that represented the relative capacities of food production in the various areas.[4] During the nineteenth century the industrialized areas developed densities of more than 450 persons per square mile. These changes resulted in very great transformations of economic and political importance. The figures in Table 1 give the larger features of the consequences of

TABLE 1*

APPROXIMATE POPULATION OF SELECTED COUNTRIES
(In Thousands)

Country	1700	1800	1850	1910	1935
United Kingdom..............	8,635	14,997	27,201	44,915	50,063
France (boundaries of 1819, 1846)	23,600	27,800	35,630	39,528	41,940
Italy (boundaries of 1910)......	11,500	16,900	21,200	34,377	42,438
Germany (boundaries of 1871)..	10,900	18,120	35,310	64,568	67,068†
Prussia (boundaries of 1846)....	5,100	8,800	....	....	....
Russia (without Finland).......	....	31,000	60,000	142,500	170,500
Japan (home islands).........	26,065‡	25,507§	31,110‖	50,980	71,968

* Source: Figures for the period 1700–1910 are from Bowden, Karpovich, and Usher, *An Economic History of Europe since 1750* (1937), pp. 20–21; figures for 1935 are from *United States Foreign Commerce Yearbook, 1937;* pp. 355–57; figures for Japan are from Ernst Schultze, *Japan als Weltindustriemacht* (Stuttgart, 1935), I, 380–86.

† Boundaries of 1935.
‡ Boundaries of 1721.
§ Boundaries of 1804.
‖ Boundaries of 1852.

the economic development. By taking population within modern boundaries, the influence of political changes in Italy and Germany is partly discounted. Unification was undoubtedly favorable to some increase in economic activity, but it was not the dominant factor. The record should be considered from the point of view of the position of France. In 1700 France was clearly the outstanding power in Europe, and the effective political influence was, of course, much greater than is suggested by the figures in the table, because Italy and Germany were divided into a large number of small and ineffective states. By 1910 France had become a second-rate power, even in terms of manpower.

4. A. P. Usher, "Population and Settlement in Eurasia," *Geographical Review,* XX (1930), 110–32; Witt Bowden, Michael Karpovich, and Abbott Payson Usher, *An Economic History of Europe since 1750* (New York, 1937), pp. 2–22.

The consequences of the generalized use of power are, however, imperfectly revealed by the direct comparison of aggregate populations. It is necessary to consider the output of mechanical energy, as this is the simplest index of the relative productive capacity of the different areas. In Table 2 are given figures for selected countries. The total output of mechanical energy has been reduced to equivalent tons of bituminous coal. For purposes of comparison, the mechanical energy has been also expressed as the work output of human labor. Such a comparison is, of course, of limited value, but the orders of magnitude are so different that the significance of the energy output is likely to be misjudged unless some rough comparison is made.

TABLE 2

Work Output of Selected Countries, 1935
(In Millions)

Country	Population	Total Mechanical Energy		
		Equivalent Tons of Coal	Equivalent Human Energy*	
			Gross Heat Energy	Effective Heat Energy
United States..........	127.2	621.6	12,432.0	2,486.4
British Isles............	50.0	226.6	4,532.1	906.4
France.'...............	41.9	54.4	1,088.0	217.6
Italy..................	42.4	11.1	222.5	44.5
Germany..............	67.0	207.0	4,141.7	828.3
U.S.S.R...............	170.5	141.5	2,831.3	566.2
Japan.................	71.9	48.8	976.0	195.2

* One ton of coal is equal to the work output of twenty persons per year. "Effective Heat Energy" is equal to 0.2 "Total Heat Energy."

The inferiority of the position of France is commandingly revealed. With a population slightly less than the population of the British Isles, France produced only one-fourth as much mechanical energy. Manpower and mechanical energy combined give a figure of 956.4 millions for the British Isles and 259.5 millions for France. When the energy output is included, the economic weakness of Italy is clearly evident.

The table also shows the other economic and political changes produced by the development of the energy economy. Germany has risen to a position of approximate equality to Britain. The absence of a clear-cut predominance of either power is perhaps the explanation of all the diplomatic and military errors of the past generation. But the commanding feature of the new world system is the emergence of the United States and Russia as primary world powers. The present position of the Soviet Union is more largely dependent upon mere manpower, but the presence of such a state even in its present position redefines completely the political problems of Europe.

The development of the United States and of Russia establishes the general character of the new world economy. The economic and political organization of these great continental areas marks the passing of the maritime world created by the age of discovery. The world economy of the present day and of the future is a world of continents. The new economy is only beginning to assume definite form. Many important areas are ineffectively developed, and scarcely any area is without major problems of political reorganization.

THE WORLD ECONOMY OF CONTINENTS

The mechanization of transport has made an end of all isolation due merely to distance and has reduced to moderate proportions the isolation due to primary mountain barriers. The conquest of mere space, begun by the railroad, has been completed by the internal combustion motor. The railroad is not economical until the volume of traffic available passes a relatively high magnitude. Many areas could not be opened by rail at remunerative rates, and in many instances there was no means of providing rail service even with public subsidy. Recent developments in motor transport by land and by air give us a fully flexible system of transport, without inconvenient differences in cost for particular volumes or classes of traffic. In the future the relative economic importance of the continents will be determined primarily by their basic resources, mineral and agricultural.

The present position of the world economy is broadly indicated by the record of energy production at the outbreak of World War II. The current position has, of course, changed, but analysis of recovery from the war and new developments still require reference to the pre-war position. The ultimate future of the world economy can best be studied in terms of resources of primary energy. Analysis of the provision of mechanical energy has been developing steadily since the world power conference of 1928. Techniques for the summation of resources have been worked out, and, though there are many imperfections in our statistics, the general features of energy distribution are sufficiently known to meet our immediate needs. Some study has been made of the available resources in human labor and in animal power, but comprehensive presentation of the resources of animal power is not satisfactory, as there are no fully comparable data for the numbers of draft animals in many parts of the world where they are especially important. Recent studies by the Department of State present estimates of available animal power, but the data have not been released for publication.

The resources in mechanical energy are the controlling factor in economic activity today, and even the energy derived from fuel wood and peat is negligible for broad analysis of the world situation, as much of the use of wood and peat is for domestic fuel. These fuels were included in the study made by the Department of State, so that we can feel assurance in the exclusion of these items until the Department of State tables are published. At the present time production of vegetable sources of fuel cannot be sufficiently concentrated to compete with coal, oil, and water power. Reserves of fissionable materials can easily be added to the energy tables as soon as we have quantitative data that are comparable.

It is perhaps desirable to emphasize the technique of analysis rather than the precision of the quantitative results. A number of problems require facilities that are beyond the resources of the individual student. Some of these problems are adequately covered by the analysis made by the Department of State, others require additional statistical work, but most of these problems affect details of the analysis and not the general picture of the world economy in either its present position or its maturer form.

Attention should be called to some of the technical problems in the preparation of Table 3. The reduction of the fuels and water powers to a common unit presents a problem, especially in respect of resources. The early tables prepared by Liesse and developed by Meisner reduced all energy to the heat energy per ton of standard bituminous coal. Water power was reduced to a coal equivalent in terms of the average coal consumption required per kilowatt hour. For a given year this coefficient is perfectly satisfactory, but for a long period of time it would make no allowance for increased efficiency in the use of coal. In the tables prepared under my direction, it was assumed that the rate of coal consumption was 1 pound per kilowatt hour, or 2.93 tons of coal per horsepower per year. This represents about the best achievement now possible; the best records in 1937 were slightly less than 1 pound per kilowatt hour. In the *Minerals Yearbook* all energy is reduced to British thermal units; this is not significantly different from the Meisner heat energy per ton of coal. The Department of State tables reduce all energy to kilowatt hours. This system of reduction presents some minor difficulties. Errors in the heat coefficient for electricity are multiplied into the major factors in the energy table instead of being confined to a minor factor.

TABLE 3

WORLD PRODUCTION OF MECHANICAL ENERGY, 1935, EXPRESSED
AS THOUSANDS OF TONS OF BITUMINOUS COAL

	Total Coal	Oil	Water Power	Total Power	Energy per Sq. Km. as Tons of Coal
The world...............	1,201,443	347,805	100,017	1,649,266	12.460
North America..........	395,174	220,501	43,944	659,619	29.447
South America...........	2,748	1,813	2,273	46,834	2.582
Europe (exc. of U.S.S.R.)..	575,587	14,587	41,938	632,112	116.518
U.S.S.R.................	100,768	38,836	1,964	141,568	6.685
Asia (exc. of U.S.S.R.).....	98,077	20,457	8,712	127,246	5.159
Africa.................	14,649	274	201	15,123	.505
Oceania.................	14,440	11,337	987	26,764	2.445
Selected countries:					
United States.............	383,476	209,285	28,935	621,696	79.308
British Isles..............	225,935	....	720	226,655	724.137
Czechoslovakia..........	16,940	28	279	17,247	123.193
France..................	46,576	114	7,740	54,430	98.784
Germany................	201,416	629	5,040	207,085	440.606
Italy...................	661	25	10,440	11,126	35.890
Poland.................	28,552	801	162	29,515	76.070
Rumania................	945	12,972	196	14,113	47.841
Spain...................	7,138	....	2,520	9,658	19.201
Yugoslavia..............	2,011	....	450	2,461	9.923
China..................	26,750	....	5	26,755	3.056
India..................	23,970	428	738	25,136	5.366
Japan (proper)...........	40,831	472	7,560	48,863	127.914
Australia................	11,840	1	67	11,908	1.566
Union of South Africa.....	13,574	....	13	13,587	11.119
Manchukuo..............	11,828	....	....	11,828	8.400

The more serious problem of reduction arises in the statement of reserves of water power. The variability in the rates of flow at different seasons presents an element of choice that admits of no wholly satisfactory solution. In the tables prepared for me the suggestions of the *Commerce Year Book* were accepted, and the potential water power was taken as 70 per cent of low water flow. Some further deductions were made in some published estimates of water power, but it seemed likely that such losses would be offset by incomplete enumeration or other errors. The tables of the Department of State use the figure for mean low water, but their tables are clearly based on new figures for the water power of the U.S.S.R. The over-all reserve of water power is taken in the present tables and in the Department of State tables as one thousand times the annual potential water power. In the tables published by Meisner, water power reserves were taken as one hundred times the annual potential power.

A different problem in the estimation of reserves is presented by petroleum. The figures given for "proved reserves" have a more restricted meaning than the similar term would have for coal or other fixed minerals. "Proved reserves" for petroleum amount to fifteen or twenty times the current product of operative wells, or, if the engineer is very optimistic, twenty-five or thirty years' supply. The Department of State figure for oil is twenty-five times the production for 1937. Recently, some oil geologists have made estimates based on the total area of sedimentary rocks related to oil formations. By these methods Wallace Pratt has held out hopes for oil reserves amounting to three hundred times the current production of 1940. Professor Kirtley F. Mather reduces this estimate to one-third on the assumption that the oil formations of Eurasia are not so good as the formations in the United States that have been used as the basis of the yield in oil. The distribution of the oil reserves is difficult, as no detailed estimates by the area method are available in print. The total amount is not very important, as the world total is less than 1 per cent of the total reserves of energy; but the immediate value of these reserves is very great. Many serious political tensions have developed in the interwar period as result of statements about our reserves that were misleading. Even if there were no deliberate intent to deceive, the episode was unfortunate and not creditable either to the experts or to the political leaders who participated in the diplomatic battle for oil.

The coal resources of the world are better known than the resources in either water power or petroleum, but there are some difficulties in the interpretation of reports. The outstanding problem is the estimate of the resources of the great coal basins in the provinces of Shensi, Shansi, and Kansu. They are not an immediate resource, and surveys are sketchy. Much of the coal that is contained in the formation affords little hope of actual commercial use at any time. But there is a great deal of coal in that region. All of it is included in the tables presented here, without any commitment about its availability. Very little of this great deposit is counted by the Department of State. The coal resources of India are not fully explored, and new information has recently been published, but the figures are not at the moment available. The coal resources of the Union of South Africa are not well known and are doubtless greater than the present figures would suggest.

When these qualifications are considered, it might seem likely that estimates of energy resources would be too uncertain to be of any value. Comparison between the tables presented here and the Department of State tables exhibits differences only in respect of items discussed above. Taking the three major sources of power, the State Department tables give coal as 70.40 per cent, oil as 0.13 per cent, and water power as 29.47 per cent of the world total. The tables used here give the following ratios: coal, 83.70 per cent; oil, 0.45 per cent; water power, 15.85 per cent. About half the difference in the percentage importance of water power is accounted for by the use of the reduced value of 70 per cent of the low water potential. The other half of the difference is due to new estimates of the water power available. There are no problems that cannot be covered by critical notes on the methods of constructing the table and the sources available. The technique that has been developed enables us to express compactly the knowledge of resources now at our command. We are entitled to accept the table of energy resources as a trustworthy basis for analysis of our position in the world as known. The group of energy tables makes it possible to describe the major features of the world economy as it is today and as it will be changed in the future by the diffusion of technology.

Unless we presume that some innovation will alter radically the importance of mechanical energy in our economy, the energy resources establish the approximate limits of the development of the various regions. Subject to some qualification for atomic energy, the resource tables indicate the potentialities of the world for at least the coming century and a half. Technical changes may alter the proportions in which the resources are used, but the power that can be produced by local resources is indicated by the tables. Movements of coal and oil in long-distance trade are largely concerned with meeting demands for domestic and commercial heating and the requirements of transportation. The effective boundaries of power zones do not coincide with present national boundaries, but the adjustments for political boundaries are not of major importance except for the relations between the Ruhr, the Belgian coal fields, and eastern France.

Tables 3, 4, and 5 give the comprehensive totals for the world by continental divisions. Data for selected countries are added to provide a basis for the appraisal of the strategic problems of the world economy.[5]

The general features of the distribution of energy production and

TABLE 4

WORLD RESOURCES OF MECHANICAL ENERGY EXPRESSED AS MILLIONS OF TONS OF BITUMINOUS COAL

	Coal	Oil	Water Power*	Total	Tons per Sq. Km.
The world..............	7,245,537.1	39,083.9	1,373,163.7	8,670,285.8	65,505.3
North America........	2,859,697.6	13,556.0	213,890.0	3,087,143.6	137,927.9
South America.......	3,116.0	5,545.0	158,220.0	166,881.0	9,199.1
Europe (exc. U.S.S.R.).	653,741.9	552.1	145,254.8	799,548.8	147,382.3
U.S.S.R.............	1,240,000.0	5,050.0	68,635.3	1,313,685.3	62,033.6
Asia (exc. U.S.S.R.)...	2,142,843.0	13,372.1	191,329.0	2,347,544.1	96,440.1
Africa..............	206,733.4	122.5	558,809.6	765,005.3	25,559.8
Oceania.............	139,405.2	862.5	50,210.0	190,477.7	17,064.1
Selected countries:					
United States........	2,378,243.4	12,390.0	123,060.0	2,513,693.4	320,665.1
British Isles.........	174,557.0	....	2,490.5	177,047.5	565,647.0
Czechoslovakia.......	30,000.0	2.1	2,930.0	32,932.1	235,229.3
France..............	17,640.0	10.0	15,822.0	33,472.0	60,747.7
Germany............	302,219.2	91.3	5,860.0	308,170.5	655,681.9
Italy...............	186.4	....	11,134.0	11,320.4	36,517.4
Poland.............	93,200.0	78.5	4,102.0	97,380.5	250,980.7
Rumania............	1,116.5	288.0	4,688.0	6,142.5	20,822.0
Spain...............	5,500.0	....	11,720.0	17,220.0	34,234.6
Yugoslavia..........	2,569.0	....	8,790.0	11,359.0	45,802.4
China..............	2,100,240.0	....	58,600.0	2,158.840.0	246,583.6
India..............	20,600.0	44.6	79,110.0	99,754.6	21,296.8
Japan (proper).......	16,407.2	53.0	25,198.0	41,658.2	109,052.4
Australia...........	139,400.0	....	1,758.0	141,158.0	18,563.7
Union of South Africa..	205,682.0	....	4,688.0	210,370.0	172,152.2
Manchukuo.........	4,804.0	....	....	4,804.0	3,400.0

*Water power is taken as one thousand times the annual coal equivalent.

resources can be most conveniently studied in the ratios given in Table 5. At the present time the production of mechanical energy is highly concentrated. Europe and the United States produced, in 1935, 76.2 per cent of the total energy output of the world, though they contained only 10.01 per cent of the total area, and about 30 per cent of the population of the world. These areas, however, con-

5. Tables 4 and 5 are taken from the complete tables published in "The Tasks of Economic History," *Journal of Economic History, Supplement*, VII (1947), 40–46. Table 3 has not previously been published, in whole or in part.

tain only 38.2 per cent of the total energy resources. The present pattern of energy production is clearly due to the earlier development of the power technology in Europe and the United States. In the course of time, within a century or more, we must presume that energy production will correspond more closely to the distribution of energy resources. Europe and the United States will ultimately be less important than they are today, but one must not presume that

TABLE 5

RATIOS BETWEEN ENERGY PRODUCTION AND RESOURCES

	PERCENTAGES OF WORLD TOTAL		
	Area	Energy (1935)	Resources
The world.............	100.000	100.000	100.000
North America........	16.924	39.995	35.606
South America........	13.706	2.840	1.924
Europe (exc. U.S.S.R.).	4.099	38.327	9.223
U.S.S.R.............	16.900	8.584	15.152
Asia (exc. U.S.S.R.)...	18.391	7.715	27.073
Africa..............	22.613	0.916	8.823
Oceania.............	8.269	1.623	2.197
Selected countries:			
United States........	5.922	37.695	28.992
British Isles.........	0.236	13.743	2.042
Czechoslovakia.......	0.106	1.046	0.380
France..............	0.416	3.300	0.386
Germany............	0.355	12.556	3.554
Italy...............	0.234	0.675	0.131
Poland..............	0.293	1.790	1.123
Rumania............	0.223	0.856	0.071
Spain...............	0.380	0.586	0.199
Yugoslavia..........	0.187	0.149	0.131
China (18 provinces)..	6.615	1.622	24.898
India...............	3.539	1.524	1.150
Japan (proper).......	0.289	2.963	0.480
Australia............	5.745	0.722	1.628
Union of South Africa..	0.923	0.824	2.426
Manchukuo..........	1.060	0.720	0.550

they will cease to be areas of very great activity. The resources now known give Europe 9.2 per cent of the energy resources to provide for the activities of 4.09 per cent of the world area. Even on a strictly proportional basis, Europe would still have a stronger position than the Soviet Union, with 16.9 per cent of the world area and 15.1 per cent of world energy resources.

South America is the poorest of all the continents in energy resources: 1.94 per cent of the total resources to provide for 13.7 per cent of the area of the world. Africa and Oceania are poorly endowed, but the Union of South Africa has an important future. Unless very great discoveries of energy resources are made in India, her prospects are poor. The undeveloped resources of China present the greatest potentiality for change that can now be foreseen. If the record is to be accepted at its face value, only Germany, Great Britain, and the United States are more richly endowed. Furthermore, despite the high ratios of concentration in Germany and Great Britain, the total mass of resources is very much smaller. China, if her resources are effectively developed and her political problems can be solved, will become an outstanding world power. The protection of her independence is therefore an issue of primary importance. It is especially important to keep constantly in mind the quantitative limitations of the energy resources that can now be commercially used in China. They are only the merest fraction of the ultimate reserves. Cautious geologists and engineers discussing immediate problems correctly give very low estimates of the "actual" or "commercially" available reserves.

PRESENT PROBLEMS OF ECONOMIC ADJUSTMENT

When we turn from the discussion of the displacements and changes of a time interval of a century and a half to the present problems of today, it is indispensable to give sharp definition to the time interval to be considered in this connection. Economic theorists are disposed to treat the "present" as a very minute interval in which nothing changes. Engineers and executives take a somewhat broader point of view, but their effective decisions are mainly concerned with a few years or a decade. It is rare to find executives of the caliber of Theodore N. Vail, who described his duty as the consideration of the problems that the company would face in the next twenty-five years. For purposes of effective analysis of underlying conditions it is essential that we should think of the present as an interval of such magnitude. We must think in terms of the present generation.

Over a long period of time, both Europe and the United States will occupy a less conspicuous place in the world than they do today. It would be a mistake, however, to presume that these changes will occur within the next two or three decades. The depression of the thirties has shaken the confidence of many, so that they are prone to see immediate and catastrophic disaster in an interruption of growth that should be distinguished from the major international readjustments that we have been considering. No study of the record of energy production since 1900 can leave one in any doubt of its relevance to any complete analysis of the depression of the thirties. But the essential feature of the period was the changes in the competitive position of the various sources of energy. The development of oil and water-power resources and changes in the technique of coal consumption exerted profound influences on the primary centers of industrialization. From 1864 to 1913 the production of coal in the world increased at an average rate of 4.4 per cent per year. Between 1913 and 1933 world production exceeded the production of 1913 only in the single year 1928, and in that year by only sixty million tons, or 3.9 per cent of the total product. It is difficult to assess the quantitative significance of the various factors involved, but the importance of such an abrupt change can scarcely be overestimated. All the great coal-producing countries felt the impact of this crisis in trade, production, and loss of employment in the mines.

There is reason to believe that this pressure upon the coal trade did not result in a net loss of effective energy disposable, but it did exert a depressing influence upon the economies of the United States, Great Britain, and Germany. Changes in the metal trades also resulted in arrested trends of physical production. Smaller tonnages of products of higher value were produced, so that conditions were complex, but the record of these basic activities indicates profound and far-reaching change. The entire group of textile industries was disturbed by developments in Japan, by changes in the price levels of cotton, and by the rise of the synthetic filaments. Despite wide diffusion of all these new techniques, there were serious geographical dislocations. To determine the precise significance of all these disturbances is difficult, but the broader analyses of the great depression recognize their importance despite the concentration of theoretical analysis upon structural defects of the individual economies. The general changes in the world economy were overlaid with specific difficulties of adjustment after World War I and with technical currency troubles accentuated by the misconceived policy on reparations.

These events were painful, and the war damage in World War II adds greatly to the difficulties of adjustment; but, despite these problems, the scale of economic activity in Europe is not likely to be greatly changed in the coming generation. The development of new energy resources will be offset in a considerable degree by increases in the consumption of heavy industrial products in the newer areas. It is commonly held that neither South Africa nor India can supply their basic needs from the local centers of production that can be opened up in the coming decades. The Soviet Union is closed to major trade movement, but there too the current standards of provision of capital goods are still low, and there is no prospect of competition of Russian products of heavy industry in the outside world. The development of China can hardly proceed rapidly enough greatly to change her industrial position with the coming generation.

The development of the oil resources of the Middle East presents uncertainties. The general features of the record suggest that these sources of energy will be used largely for transportation and for heating. Nothing in the history of the older oil regions justifies an expectation of any major diversion of oil to industrial use. Natural gas has recently become an important source of industrial energy in some of the oil fields of the United States. It can certainly develop importance in any oil fields capable of using such energy. The amount of energy, however, is small—about one-fourth the total energy of the petroleum and gas combined.

In some of the Central and South American oil fields gas and oil might become a source of power of considerable local importance, but costs would be high and would hamper any substantial industrial development.

The political consequences of the economic changes are more extensive and more disturbing than the economic consequences. Despite the magnitude of the basic changes, the displacements of population would be small and spread over long periods of time. Some regions will face readjustments, but, except for the intrusion of stresses due to war, none of the readjustments should entail reductions in essential standards of living. The transformation of the world economy has made the political organization of Europe hopelessly obsolete. Conditions in Europe itself are now inconsistent with the aggressively nationalistic units of which Europe is now composed. But even if these internal difficulties could be overcome, the development of the United States and the Soviet Union dwarfs even the largest European states and leaves them without effective power in the political world. As truly independent units most of the states of Europe have become negligible quantities. It is a strange indication of the shallowness of much nineteenth-century glorification of nationalism that such independent sovereignty has already become an empty formalism for many if not most of these states.

TECHNOLOGY AND INTERNATIONAL RELATIONS

The nineteenth century was marked by the culmination of a long period of political development toward nationalism. To many it seemed to be the triumphant close of a long struggle for liberty and independence, and there was a tendency to presume that political development need not proceed beyond the definitive establishment of a system of states based upon the principles of nationalism and democracy. In this idealistic interpretation of history the economic functions of the state and the economic organization of the region were neglected and underestimated. In Great Britain, France, Germany, Italy, and Spain there was economic foundation for organized political life that found no counterpart in the Balkan States that were formed after the decline of Turkish power in Europe. Furthermore, nationalism had widely different implications for the development of the state system in south-central and southeastern Europe.

In Germany and in Italy nationalism had been a constructive force, leading to the organization of many small units into relatively large units that were much more satisfactory bases for economic administration. In south-central and southeastern Europe nationalism assumed the form of a demand for cultural autonomy with little or no regard for economic geography or administrative convenience. This movement threatened the Dual Monarchy and created tensions among the Balkan States that obstructed the effective integration of the area within the European economy.

This association of cultural groups with the principle of nationalism is a striking illustration of the degree to which ideological tendencies are built around concepts without any regard for the totality of economic and social circumstances that alone can give meaning to the concept. Even in the nineteenth century, the pressing need was for more political integration rather than for the disintegration set in motion by the racial concepts that were built around language and other cultural habits and customs. It was a perverse and unsound inference from the principles of liberalism.

Pan-Germanism and Pan-Slavism seemed to promise more, because there was a demand for "liberation" of subject populations and emphasis on the enlargement of the primary states. These movements, however, were threatening to the Dual Monarchy and to some of the Balkan States. The net effect of racialism in Europe was divisive and destructive. As a principle it could lead only to the progressive segregation of the smaller culture groups, which from every point of view was unfortunate for them and for the world.

The Serbian contribution to the initiation of World War I was this issue of racial "liberation" or "redemption." Although it cannot be regarded as an initial or major war aim of any of the major powers, it was forced upon the Allies partly by the activities of the various dissident groups in the Dual Monarchy and partly by the unfortunate inclusion of "self-determination" among the "Fourteen Points." The extensive application of this principle in the treaties of peace was certainly one of the greatest mistakes of the war. The state system which Britain, France, and the United States had hoped to preserve was impaired and weakened, so that the temptation to adopt aggressive policies toward weak neighbors was greatly increased.

This principle obstructed constructive adaptation to basic changes in Europe, and in the interwar period the contagion spread. The development of antagonisms between the Arabs and the Jews in Palestine, and between Hindus and Moslems in India, was fostered by this dangerous principle. All this racialism is based on intolerance: intolerance of differences in religion, intolerance of differences in speech, intolerance of social habits and customs. In so far as such intolerance represents an abuse of power, the proper remedy is to be found in the reform of the state to prevent such abuse of power. Liberty cannot be achieved for anyone by the progressive segregation of minorities.

THE OLD BALANCE OF POWER IN THE NEW WORLD ECONOMY

The unification of Germany and the development of her primary energy resources made her the outstanding state in Continental Europe. After the Franco-Prussian War there could be no serious doubt of the primacy of her political importance, but Bismarck was patient and disposed to make haste slowly. The position of Germany was clearly different, but there were few overt signs of the change in the balance of power. After the retirement of Bismarck, Prussian diplomacy was conducted with less discretion and restraint. A revision of alliances began which reflected the changes in the balance of power. Prussian concern for the position of Austria in the Balkans led to increased tension with Russia and ultimately to the abandonment of the alliance with Russia.

Relations between Great Britain and Germany became less cordial, and ultimately a new association between Great Britain and

France was developed. Serious conflicts in Africa were composed, and by 1905 Britain and France had formed an association which was in effect a defensive alliance. The alliance between France and Russia created a combination which on paper at least offered substantial guaranties for the preservation of peace in Europe and maintenance of the status quo. The alliance of Germany with Austria and Italy provided some balance for the forces arrayed against her. The weakness of this political rearrangement lay in the palpable inferiority of France and the ineffectiveness of the British preparations for any major military operation on land.

The most difficult economic problem was the effective development of the great heavy-industry area on the frontiers of Germany, France, and Luxembourg. French interests were associated with the German interests through interconnections among the larger corporations. A compensatory flow of coal and ore made it possible to achieve full utilization of transport facilities and to give each area a share in the primary iron and steel products. These private corporate adjustments were sufficiently satisfactory to keep the major economic issues out of high politics.

The development of a customs union at this time might have been of great significance, but there would have been difficulties. In fact, this means of reducing trade restrictions was confined to Luxembourg and some of the old free cities like Hamburg.

IMPERIALISM

The desire to maintain the status quo in Europe made the colonial sphere an important opportunity for political change. It is perhaps not too much to say that the development of imperial control was the most evident diplomatic reaction to the changes in the effective structure of the world economy. The policies of Germany, France, and Japan were in part an imitation of Great Britain, in part an application of somewhat naïve concepts of autarchy on a broader geographic basis. It was presumed that industrialized areas would find significant and satisfactory markets in the undeveloped regions of the tropics and subtropics. These areas would not compete in the production of industrial items and would supply the necessary raw materials without any interposing of fiscal barriers against the mother-country.

There were monopolistic elements in overseas development that afforded some support for this type of neomercantilism, but it is difficult to believe that this analysis of economic conditions was sound. The record of overseas trade and administration is clear cut. The volume of trade was relatively small, and the fiscal burdens were disproportionately large. Whatever the importance of trade in particular tropical products, it is quite clear that overseas trade was not in any sense a substitute for European and North American markets.

Be that as it may, Germany and France embarked upon a program of colonial expansion: Germany, to build up prestige suitable to her new position in Europe; France, in hopes of offsetting weaknesses in Europe by the acquisition of dominions that would make good a deficit in manpower even if it did not yield any commanding opportunities for economic expansion. The personal adventure of Leopold II of Belgium cannot be omitted, though the motivation seems to have been largely economic.

In eastern Asia the weakness of the Chinese Empire invited attention from Europe, from Japan, and from Russia. At one time the stage seemed to be set for a partition of China into spheres of influence that were perhaps expected to become areas of exclusive overseas administration. There was a reaction against this policy, and it was finally recognized that the integrity of China proper should be respected. Manchuria, southeastern Asia, and parts of Mongolia were left open for competitive political and economic activity.

It seemed to be assumed that the Old World, with the exception of China, was to be ruled by some European power. The world economy would thus produce a group of empires in which a European industrial area controlled an array of overseas possessions, primarily devoted to agriculture and the production of crude minerals. The New World, under the shelter of the Monroe Doctrine, was to consist of an array of independent states dependent for protection against Europe upon the ministrations of the United States. Some unfortunate episodes created suspicions about the complete disinterestedness of the United States. In some areas the political independence of the state was clearly no more than a façade for control by large corporate interests, which enjoyed immunities from control that they could not have experienced in the dependency of some major power.

On the surface, the record of imperial development from 1880 to 1914 exhibits the complacency of Europe at its worst and furnishes a vast array of material for the criticism of the political and economic achievements of the Western cultures. But it is quite important not to confine attention to the surface of the record. Contacts between cultures are commonly fruitful and stimulating to both, and the experiences of overseas administrators was no exception to the rule. Although many approached the task in a spirit of boredom, complacency, and condescension, there were vigorous minds that reacted vitally to the problems presented. It was impossible to conduct affairs upon the basis provided by Victorian liberalism or the Code Napoléon.

Overseas administration presented in concrete form the essential problem of liberal statecraft—the protection of the rights of social groups at low cultural levels. This right had been asserted by Grotius in the essay *On the Freedom of the Seas*. This principle had been the basis of all overseas development throughout the sixteenth and seventeenth centuries. It was the basis of the entire legal structure underlying the African possessions of the European powers.

Curiously enough the full importance of this phase of overseas administration was less clearly appreciated when the native states were substantially developed, as in India. The scattered agents of the great trading companies were hardly likely to feel that the native economy required protection against intrusive influences. In Africa the relatively primitive natives stood in a very different relation to the Europeans, and it soon became clear that the native economy should be protected and preserved. There emerged a conscious understanding of the problems of a plural society; that is, of a society consisting of groups separated by such differences of culture that each group possessed a distinct and separate social and economic life. The task of overseas administration is to assure freedom for development and economic opportunity for both the European and the native economies.

Overseas administration demonstrates the necessity of recognizing that a state may not and, in fact, is not likely to consist of a homogeneous population. Many of the worst errors in social policy have been based on the assumption or assertion of the converse doctrine. Religious intolerance, "racial" intolerance, and cultural intolerance all rest upon the false assumption that there is and ought to be a socially and culturally homogeneous group.

The United States possesses a problem in plural administration that is scarcely less difficult than the problems of the Union of South Africa. The problems of the diverse culture group of India differ only in details from the problems of minorities in Europe. Overseas administration does not present distinctive problems, but we can frequently see the mistakes of others more clearly than we see our own. Much time might be saved if we were to recognize that all these problems of the dependencies are general problems that appear in every society in some form.

The structure of the British Commonwealth of Nations is also of significance for any student of a state system for the modern world. The British Commonwealth has developed a new concept of independence and legislative autonomy. The self-governing dominions have legislative autonomy, but they do not possess sovereignty in the Austinian sense. They are not entitled to ignore the rights or acts of other dominions. The achievement of federal union in the Union of South Africa was a notable recognition that small states cannot wisely retain their independence when the economy of which they are a part requires some central administration. Similar accomplishments are possible elsewhere.

TECHNOLOGY AND WARFARE

The Industrial Revolution exerted only modest influence on the conduct of warfare until the development of the metal trades began to produce marked effect upon the range, accuracy, and rapidity of fire in the various classes of ordnance. In their entirety these improvements in firearms represent a slow accumulation of inventions which exhibited important results only in late stages of the process. The chronology of the development is complicated because the timing of change varied considerably among the different classes of ordnance.

Improvements fall into four general classes: (1) changes in design, (2) the introduction of interchangeable parts manufacture, (3) the production and fashioning of special steels, and (4) the introduction of new explosives better suited to the requirements of ordnance. It is dangerous to attempt any appraisal of the relative significance of these various elements, because all were important. The improvement of steelmaking was certainly one of the key problems. The Krupp process for crucible steel was a factor in the development of Prussian ordnance in the mid-century, and Bessemer's attention was first attracted to steelmaking by the deficiencies of contemporary ordnance. But the record shows clearly that all classes of change were essential to any major accomplishment.

In actual military operations our Civil War and the war between Prussia and Austria mark the beginnings of new fire power. The smooth bores finally gave way to rifles. The smooth-bore muskets were inaccurate even at 200 yards. "The new rifles were sighted up to 1,000 yards, and were fairly accurate at 650. Thus, the distance which assaulting troops must cover under fire was more than quadrupled. . . . Frontal attacks became so difficult that adequately defended fronts were almost impossible to break."[6] At the outset the infantry rifle outranged much of the field artillery, so that operations became very ill balanced.

The great increase in the fire power of the infantry led to more use of protective cover, notably in the Civil War and in the Boer War. The short wars in 1866 and 1870–71 were not fully indicative of some of these changes because of the overwhelming superiority of the Prussian army. Trench warfare developed at an early stage of World War I, precisely because the fire power of the lighter weapons had developed much faster than the effectiveness of artillery. Field pieces that were heavy enough to penetrate the defensive system were too immobile to participate in a war of movement. World War I brought to a close the transitional period that had begun about 1860.

The layman must defer to experts in such matters, and it is perhaps dangerous to accept broad generalization even from experts. However, some of the commentators on military development present a very plausible synthesis of the elements underlying the war of movement that was so conspicuous in World War II.

"Technically speaking, the chief lesson of the present war is the triumph of the gun over individual weapons, a triumph made possible by the internal combustion engine which we have already called the iron horse. By 'gun' we mean any team weapon, i.e., one which cannot be carried and fought by a single man on foot or mounted on a horse. Such weapons, for the first time in recorded history, now dominate the technique of land warfare."[7]

This development in the use of artillery has been made possible by the mobility given even heavy pieces of motorized equipment and by the freedom of movement given the men associated with these weapons. Modern warfare is thus based on motor vehicles, tanks, and airplanes. Mechanized transport has become a vital factor on the battlefield itself.

In two respects these changes exert a commanding influence on the

6. H. Nickerson, *Arms and Policy* (New York, 1945), pp. 14–15.
7. *Ibid.*, pp. 247–48.

structure of the state. Industrial activity is more closely associated with military activity than ever before. The war of rapid movement requires more space than the wars fought with foot soldiers. Even a country the size of France has scarcely space enough for the conduct of war. Defense in depth, as now understood, would bring a large portion of the northern industrial area within the area of military action almost at the outset of any war. Warfare requires space on a continental scale.

When the airplane is used independently of land or naval forces for the bombing of military or nonmilitary targets, a new array of questions arises which affect very deeply the conduct of war. Attacks on transportation and on munitions plants raise the question of efficiency. This is essentially a question of fact. Is it possible to interfere sufficiently with production and transport to justify the cost in manpower and material? One may well doubt the adequacy of some of the answers that have been given. One has an impression that postwar study of records leads to much reclassification of the results on different classes of targets. Significant use of bombing outside the zones of specific military operations will probably develop on lines very different from the original beliefs of the advocates of the independent use of air power.

Bombing of areas occupied largely or in part by civilians raises problems of military and social policy rather than technical or military problems in the strict sense. If we think of warfare as an instrument of policy, and not as an end in itself, the long-run effects of bombing civilians must be considered. It is perhaps justifiable to make it clear that no country can make war without incurring a risk of serious war damage. But ruthless destruction of productive and socially necessary property opens up border-line questions which it is not easy to answer. If the rational purpose of war is to lay foundations for a better peace than existed before, then vengeful or reckless bombing of civilians is irrational and indefensible in terms of long-range policy. We cannot wisely use all the powers of destruction now at our command.

The impact of the Industrial Revolution on naval operations was more evident and more immediate than the effects upon land. The technique of building iron and steel ships was taken up by the navies of the world at a relatively early date, and the new materials were soon used as a means of protecting the vessels against gunfire. In a rudimentary form the new potentialities were demonstrated by the

"Merrimac" and the "Monitor." A combination of armor with large, turret-mounted guns produced the battleship of the later age.

The immediate consequence of these developments was to create a powerful economic basis for the naval superiority that England had achieved before the passing of sailing ships. For a generation or two England was easily able to outbuild any possible rival for sea power.

It is not easy to analyze the effect of the totality of economic change upon sea power. In the older world economy of maritime fringes, sea power was obviously of very great importance, even if one discounts the exaggerations of some of the disciples of Admiral Mahan. In the present world economy of continental masses, sea power is still of very great significance. Much essential interregional trade must be moved on the shipping lanes of the oceans. Oceanic commerce has grown in proportion to the inland commerce of the continents. The protection of the sea lanes is no less important than in the eighteenth and nineteenth centuries, but it would be an oversimplification to assume that, either in the past or at present, naval supremacy offered a simple and direct means of supremacy in the world. Land armies cannot be dismissed lightly as localized forces that can be held in check by the more universal form of power expressed as naval supremacy.

The perfection of the submarine and the development of naval air forces has created a new array of naval potentialities. All the older functions of naval activity emerge in new forms of greater striking power, and some new functions appear. Naval activity against coast defense has assumed an unexpected potency, with or without landing operations. Amphibious operations offer entirely new opportunities for the associated use of land and naval forces.

The present competition for prestige between the United States and the Soviet Union emphasizes anew the conflicting claims of sea power and land power. The older contests between Great Britain and France, and between Great Britain and Germany, were based upon profoundly different conditions. There was enough dependence upon water-borne commerce both in France and in Germany to give meaning to a threat of blockade. The effectiveness of blockades was perhaps exaggerated, but a blockade could be established that would subject northwestern Europe to serious pressure. In the nineteenth century, even if it were not in itself a decisive factor in victory, sea power could create conditions which would make victory on land easier to achieve. It is difficult to believe that a policy of blockade could contribute much in any conflict between the United States and the Soviet Union. In all probability any conflict between these powers would ultimately become a struggle for control of strategic areas in Europe or in Asia. Every advantage of position would be held by the Soviet Union. Sea power would be necessary to the United States, but it would contribute little to victory.

INDUSTRIAL POTENTIALS AND WAR POTENTIALS

The great increase in the significance of industrial activity for war potentialities leads many to presume that the relationship is simple and direct. This is certainly far from the truth. Military potentials involve many factors that are not involved in any way in the economic position of a region, and even the limitations that would be effective in the economic administration of resources would not be limiting factors in military policy.

Geographic features that are of little importance in time of peace may become fatal sources of weakness in war. The location of primary centers of industry in France leaves them exposed to occupation at the outset of any war which involves any penetration of French territory. Poland and Czechoslovakia were so exposed to attacks from different frontiers that the defenders at one frontier were in effect outflanked by attack from the other front. No war of movement could possibly be contained within the limits essential to the defense of the territory. Small states like Belgium, Holland, and the Scandinavian countries had long since ceased to be viable except as part of a European system guaranteed by a balance of power among the large units in the state system. The war potential of many states may be very much less than their economic potential.

Conversely, the war potential may be greater than the economic potential. Japan affords the most important illustration. We may turn to Table 6 for basic data. The Japanese figures are for the home islands; they exclude Korea, Formosa, Sakhalin, and Manchukuo. Except for the larger population, France made a better showing of primary economic activity than Japan. This economic comparison includes a great deal of economic activity that was based on subsidies whose underlying purpose was military. Merchant shipping, the iron and steel industry, coal-mining, power generation, and heavy chemicals were all profoundly affected by direct or indirect subsidies which carried the development of these industries beyond the limits that would have been imposed by a strictly commercial policy in resource administration.

But such a comparison is misleading. It gives an essentially false impression of the issues really at stake. The position of Japan in the world as a whole is less important than its position in eastern Asia. The fact that it is the most highly industrialized area in the Eastern world is more important than any comparison with Europe. For any conflict in the eastern Pacific area Japan was in a position to concentrate imposing forces. Effective military and naval power is in part a function of distance. Comparisons are, therefore, useful only when the problem is specified by the designation of the location of the likely area of conflict.

Many early estimates of the war potential of Japan failed to give

TABLE 6

RELATIVE ECONOMIC POSITION OF FRANCE AND JAPAN PROPER

	PER CENT OF WORLD TOTAL	
	France	Japan
Power locally produced (1935)......	3.30	2.96
Total power resources.............	0.38	0.48
World factory output (1937).......	5.25	3.28
Population (1935).................	41,940,000	71,968,000

due weight to the resources controlled in Korea and Manchuria, to say nothing of resources of China administered by Japanese-controlled corporations or interests friendly to Japan. After the occupation of parts of China, important minerals were directly controlled by Japan. Analysis of all these elements of economic strength required comparisons with the Asiatic countries as well as with the European establishments in eastern Asia. The sum total of these war potentials was very great.

Furthermore, the proportion of industrial production that can be diverted to military requirements varies somewhat in different economies. In a large area, such as the United States, transportation in war as in peace consumes a larger proportion of fuel and material than would be necessary to serve the economy of Japan. Even if there were no differences in standards of consumer demand for fuels and products of heavy industry, a much smaller percentage of production would be available for military purposes in the United States than would be the case in Japan.

The length of communication lines for the war in the Pacific imposed heavy burdens on the United States. Each actual combatant in the United States forces required more supply and maintenance services than a Japanese combatant. Some of the disparities in total resources were thus offset by geographic features of the economies themselves or of the military problem as defined by the precise areas of conflict. War potential is undoubtedly dependent upon economic resources, but it cannot be accurately appraised by a mere statistical summation of basic resources.

War potential should not be identified with war power. The actual military power of a country must include a correct appraisal of the entire preparatory effort: the character, organization, and training of the armed forces, the equipment provided, and the quality of leadership. Whatever one may feel about war as an instrument of policy, it is a mistake not to recognize that successful warfare, whether defensive or offensive, requires skilful leadership. The records of warfare are replete with instances of disastrous errors, and desperate situations have been saved by some error of the offense; but success has usually been achieved by skilful leadership rather than by mere weight of manpower or industrial power. It would be very dangerous for a country to assume that wars are going to be won hereafter on the assembly lines of its industrial plants.

AVIATION AND INTERNATIONAL RELATIONS

By William Fielding Ogburn

THE question to be discussed in this chapter is: "Have the relationships of nations become different because of aviation, and, if so, what are these changes in international relations that are due to these inventions?" We shall also speculate about the effects that may be expected in the future, and we shall relate aviation to some present-day policies of different states. Aviation is a major invention, and all its effects upon international affairs are too numerous to catalogue in a short paper. From such a possible catalogue we select the major effects. The word "aviation" can be extended to include guided missiles and rockets. The discussion falls naturally into two parts: war effects and peacetime effects. In presentation we shall not follow such a dichotomy but shall treat the influences topically.

THE TECHNIQUE OF WAR

Aviation produced a revolution in warfare. An outstanding effect has been to bring the attack to the civilian population of congested areas and to factories and their products. Therefore, the airplane has contributed more to offense than to defense. The equilibrium between attack and defense has been unbalanced. At present the civilian population and industry are without adequate defense. However, our problem is not to describe the effect of aviation on the methods of war but only in so far as the new warfare changes international relations. I think that the threat of bombing from the air will have the effect of scattering somewhat the population and the location of industry if wars continue, if bombing is not restricted, and if an adequate defense is not found. But this is a domestic, not a foreign, policy. As to foreign relations, aviation, under present conditions, renders states with large concentrations of population and of industry highly vulnerable. Thus England, unless most excellently defended, becomes subject to much destruction, and her strength in a fight is weakened. She is no longer an impregnable fortress surrounded by a large moat of ocean water. In international relations a country with many compact cities becomes weakened thereby to some extent. At one time cities were a symbol of mechanization and mechanical power and were a measure of the strength of a state. They are now also, but in addition they are an indication of vulnerability, and the net effect is a weakened military position.

An interesting question is whether aviation will lead to a co-operative effort of states to restrict bombing by air. The atomic bomb led to such an effort. It may be that in the future an attempt will be made to restrict the dropping of chemical and other kinds of bombs from airplanes. These chemical bombs are not so destructive as atom bombs, but they cause much devastation. Any effort to limit their use would probably first be directed toward restricting them to certain military objectives, such as large factories essential to the war effort, key agencies, means of transportation, and stock piles. Cities without such military objectives would be declared free from attack. However, there is not at the present time, that is, since the airplane, any movement in this direction. Yet in the future it is quite possible that the effect of the air bomber will be to stimulate a co-operative effort to control its use, even though there is a strong probability that such an agreement would be broken during war.

We have been speaking of the effect of air bombing on civilian population. With military objectives there is the same danger in concentration. For instance, canals and naval bases and, of course, air bases are better protected if they are somewhat scattered. In the case of canals, alternative routes are desired, and their value is lessened because air affords another method of transportation. Concentrations of ships are similarly more vulnerable.

At the present time attack by air is less risky and more efficient if the attack is from air bases near the enemy. The United States attacked Japan regularly from the Marianas, about fifteen hundred miles away, with our B-29's. But such a distance is far for the fighter planes to give protection. Hence the policy of the powers is to acquire bases near the potential enemy, which acquisition often puts them into the territory of other states. One of the policies, then, of a major state is to acquire air bases under the sovereignty of another state. Such an acquisition can be made only by virtue of influence, which may be expressed in various ways. Policies as to the methods used in acquiring air bases is important for the relations of nations. They may be taken ruthlessly or they may be acquired by friendly means. International relations are affected by the moral nature of these policies. The danger to the country furnishing air bases may be restricted to the local area of the bases, which may be fairly large or scattered. Competition for an air base between nations, as in the case of Iceland, is an important source of friction.

Generalizing on this concept of the location of air bases, we may expect that each power will struggle to acquire bases close to their potential enemies. With the range which the airplane now has, this struggle for overlapping areas of potential air bases becomes world wide for the great powers of today.

The suitable location of air bases varies according to the type of aircraft. Bases for launching rockets must be very close; for jet fighters they may be more distant; for bombers, still more distant. Developments will change these requirements. Greater ranges are expected for rockets. But even if bombers could fly twenty thousand miles nonstop, and fighters too, there would still be economy and efficiency in having air bases relatively close to the enemy's territory.

This need of having bases of attack distant from the homeland and near areas to be attacked or guarded is not new. It is an old problem for a naval power, for big ships reduced distances in water. To Britain, the sea power, Singapore was well located. The airplane changes and magnifies the problem of bases for attack.

Other international effects of the airplane in war on policy and position will be discussed under other topics.

THE PROTECTION OF DISTANCE AND NATURAL BARRIERS

Much of the influence of aviation on international relations flows from its speed, which lessens the time required to travel great distances. Distance is an isolating factor, as is a high mountain barrier or a great body of water. The lessening of the barrier of distance has an effect of breaking down the isolation of a region. Fast ships achieve the same result. Columbus discovered America and broke its isolation only after ships became larger and freed from the necessity of oars. The airship travels through the air, which is a more universal medium than either land or water.

The United States offers a good illustration of how policy in international relations is affected by the attribute which an airplane has of conquering distance. With friendly small countries to the north and south and two wide oceans on each side, the United States once found a measure of security, especially as the British navy was friendly. The United States did not have to seek many raw materials in other lands. Since the resources of our favored land were great, the discussions in Congress and in newspaper editorials, as a result, were largely upon domestic affairs. We had no military alliances. The policy based on this situation was labeled "isolationism."

The influence of aviation is to weaken the policy of isolationism, though there are many other factors that affect it. The policy was weakened by the outcome of the Spanish-American War, which gave us commitments as far away as the Philippines. The increasing dependence on rubber and tin, products which we did not have in the United States and which we obtained from great distances, was also weakening our isolation policy. Europe was becoming closer by virtue of faster ocean-going ships. But with this trend came eventually the air bomber with a ten-thousand-mile nonstop flight and the aircraft carrier. In future world wars it seems almost certain that our civilian population will experience some bombing. Therefore, we are forced to take into consideration for policy-making the conditions over the world out of which world wars might originate. Aviation also favors foreign investment and the acquisition of needed resources in distant lands. The airplane has, then, given the coup de grâce to the old-time isolationism of the nineteenth century. Ideologies are slow to die. Hence isolationism as a social philosophy hangs on with some modification in its application. The neo-isolationists today in the United States are reluctant to break away fully and oppose, for instance, attempts to keep the influence of potential enemies out of western Europe.

It is interesting to recall that the aviator who demonstrated most dramatically the ability of the airplane to fly the oceans and thus break down the isolationism of the United States became one of the leaders of the "America First" movement to which the isolationists flocked.

At the close of World War I, it was a long flight and a hazardous one for the airplane from London to Paris. Therefore, few thought of the airplane as modifying our isolationist policy. Most of us look backward at tradition and do not recognize that inventions evolve. If there had been widespread knowledge of the influence of technology on society and of the high probability that the airplane would quickly and safely fly the Atlantic Ocean, the isolationist senators who fought the entry of the United States into the League of Nations might not have been successful, and United States foreign policy would have been different.

The airplane lessens the protection from mountains and waters as well as from distance. Britain is a good illustration. Water barriers have long protected her shores from invasion. Being protected, Britain was freer to pursue a policy of joining either side in a European conflict, that is, the side that opposed an aggressive state with the ambition to dominate Europe. But present-day Britain is forced to seek the friendship of the states of western Europe. Rockets can now be shot across the water barrier, and her navy cannot protect her from them. So Britain needs also a border of friendly states as a protection against rockets if not against air bombers. To be protected against air attack, a zone is needed much broader than the width of the states of western Europe that impinge on the Atlantic Ocean. In other words, neither the island position of Britain nor her position with reference to Europe is a protection against the air attack, and her policies for security, whatever they may be, must adjust to this fact. The policy of isolationism as a defense measure of Britain is gone under the impact of aviation.

THE SHIFTS OF POWER

History is a record of the struggle of powers for dominance. This leadership in power has shifted from one state to another. From Athens to Rome to Spain to France to Britain has been its course. These shifts in power are due to various factors; often explanations are in terms of technology. It is said that agricultural inventions and bigger boats favored the shift of power from the Mediterranean to northwestern Europe. Certainly the steam engine gave Britain for a time a differential advantage.

A natural question, then, is: "Does the airplane tend to give power to any class of states more than to another?" One answer is that aviation adds to the strength of large states and diminishes relatively the strength of small states.

The addition to the power of large states lies in part in the requirements of production of aircraft. In general, a nation must be able to make steel from iron ore to produce airplanes. Italy in the 1920's and 1930's did make airplanes without much of a steel industry. She was able to do this from scrap which was bought from other countries and which was melted down in furnaces, heated by hydroelectric power. Italy did not make airplanes from the products of her own blast furnaces, for she does not have the iron ore or the coking coal to make steel from the raw materials. Italy could therefore stock-pile airplanes during peacetime, but she was not in a position to replace them in war.

Not all large nations can make airplanes, and those which do not would not have their strength augmented much by aviation. Brazil is a large state territorially, though at present not particularly large in population; but, as far as we know, it is lacking in the coal necessary to produce much steel.

The might of India and China may be expected to increase because of the airplane, but their industrialization has not been extensive enough up to the present time to manufacture airplanes. A considerable understructure of tool- and machine-making is necessary for producing modern airplanes.

The number of airplanes needed for modern war is of course relative. But with a large power like the United States, which produced 96,359 aircraft in one year (1944), a smaller state such as France or Poland would have difficulty in meeting such competition.

Airplanes in peacetime are used more by a nation with a large expanse of territory than by a state of small area. The competition of aviation with railroads in passenger traffic is keener when the distance is over three hundred miles. The Netherlands can run an airline from the home country to parts of her overseas possessions and to other countries, as can Britain, and thus gain experience with aviation. But a large state like the United States will probably get more passengers and freight and make more flights between countries than will a small state. Opportunity for experience with airplanes is therefore greater in a state with a large area.

The airplane also has the potentiality of increasing the unity of a large country. A large area sometimes has highly developed localisms, and there is need for greater unification. For example, in the United States, the states of the Pacific Coast, before the airplane and when railroad travel was slow, were somewhat like a different country. They were far away from the center of population, with a large semidesert intervening. Airplanes bring the population of these Far Western states much closer to the populous eastern states. Even the Middle West, which is one thousand to fifteen hundred miles from the Atlantic Coast, is said to have attitudes on international relations that are different from those of people on the coasts. Of course, the airplane is only one of many inventions whose influence is in the direction of unification. The telephone and the radio may be even more influential.

The United States has an extraordinarily highly developed inter-communication system, much more so than Russia, India, or China. The airplane may, then, do more in unifying these countries than in the United States. The problem of unification is not so great in a small country. Hence the airplane favors the large state.

But it is in fighting potential that the airplane brings the great advantage to the large power over the small state. The big fellow, in general, has the advantage over the little fellow. But sometimes a little nation has combated successfully a larger state; populous states have on occasion had difficulties in getting their large armies transported and fed; and small nations have at times held mountain passes against very large numbers, especially when the fighting weapons were hand ones. But with very destructive bombs carried in planes that fly over mountains and forts, the small nation has little chance against such a blitzkrieg. It is not the airplane alone, however, that widens the gap in power between large and small states. The influence of the armored tank and of mechanization in general operates to make the big state more powerful in war relative to the small state. The coming of the airplane gives meaning to the quotation, "To him that hath shall be given."

The increased differential between the great power and the small state is clearly seen by comparing the power of Russia with that of Finland or Rumania or Belgium. The differential may also be increased between Russia and the larger European states, such as France and Italy and Poland and possibly, in the not-too-distant future, Germany.

Indeed, today the average European state seems small in power as compared to Russia and the United States. Before the twentieth century every great power was European. Prior to World War I and even to World War II the commanding position of the European states in the world at large was obvious. Of the eight great powers before World War I—Britain, France, Italy, Germany, Austria-Hungary, Russia, Japan, and the United States—five were wholly in Europe. After World War II and the airplane, no great power is altogether in Europe. Germany might become again a power of considerable magnitude. If she had won in World War II, probably much of Europe would have been integrated economically and militarily under her leadership and would thus have become a superpower. Parenthetically, the railroad greatly aided Germany in her striking power. If transportation alone dictated a large state, Europe would be expected even now to be united.

Two of these great powers have, after World War II, become superpowers, leaving the one-time great powers behind in military might. This commanding lead in rank of the two superpowers is due to many factors, as, for instance, the growth of industry and population and the weakening effects of wars. But certainly one of the influences is air power.

The ranking of the military powers is different now from the rank of fifty or one hundred years ago. Various factors have contributed to this re-ranking, an important one being the spread of the steam and steel inventions from Britain to other nations which have iron and coal supplies. Also important was the growth of populations, which has generally been associated with the spread of the Industrial Revolution. Among these forces, some part has been played by aviation as analyzed in the preceding paragraphs. But, whatever the factors, the mid-twentieth century finds two superpowers, each concerned with affiliating with them the near-by states. We shall utilize this alignment as a framework for futher discussion of the influence of aviation upon international relations.

THE SUPERPOWERS AND THEIR AFFILIATES

Ours is a world today with two great powers on opposite sides of the earth as are the North and the South poles. The world in a political sense may be turning around the axis joining these two great polar states. We call international policies, then, "bipolar." It is a picturesque term. These two great powers are like the poles of a magnet around which cluster many of the lesser states of the world. We thus refer to the arrangement as a "bipolar pattern." This pattern comes about by virtue of geographical position and also the stage in the evolution of states in size in which there are two great military powers who have pulled out ahead of other military powers, though not from other states in population.

The present bipolar power pattern seems to derive in some measure from the desire of each power not to have adjoining territory used as possible bases for attack and invasion by potential enemies. Such was the purpose of the Monroe Doctrine in the United States a century and a quarter ago. Russia, much invaded in the first half of the present century from border states on many sides, does not want her border states to be under the influence of possible invaders. The necessary search for safety in the warring Europe of preceding centuries, when several states of nearly equal power lay side by side, led to alliances. But in the middle twentieth century, when the differential between the two great powers and the small powers has been increased, the old policy of alliances between more or less equal powers does not apply. Rather, the great states seek "alliances" with the border states. But, since the differential in military power is great between the large central state and the surrounding border states, the arrangement is not as an alliance between equals but tends to be a domination of the smaller power by the larger.

This characterization of a great state and its satellites may not be strictly accurate. The affiliation may be one of mutual advantage, as in the case of Canada and the United States. The nature of this affiliation may vary widely from dictation to a friendly co-operation based on mutual interests.

The question before us is how this bipolar pattern of great states with friendly border states is affected by the airplane. That the airplane was an influence in widening the distance in power potential between the large state and the small states and in augmenting the importance of the big state has been shown. But given a great state in a center of weaker states, by its geographical position, the idea of a zone of security of small border states can exist without the invention of the airplane. When President Monroe enunciated his famous doctrine, there were no airplanes. The question is: "What effect does aviation have on this policy of being surrounded by a zone of friendly states?" The airplane seems to have an effect on the size of this zone of security around the powerful center state. The airplane is, of course, new, and its influence has not yet been worked out. But it would seem that in the future a wider zone of security would be wanted because of the long-range bomber. We know that the size of the boat had a good deal to do with the size of the zone of water needed to offer security. Until the end of the Middle Ages the small boats traveled mostly along the shore. But even when big boats were crossing the Atlantic Ocean frequently and easily, there was a measure of security to the United States because of the size of the two oceans on each side. As better navigation on water affected the zone of security afforded by water, so it would seem that the airplane would mean a larger zone than would be needed when land transportation was by highway or railway.

It also might be argued that the zone would have to be so large that the concept would eventually no longer hold, since some planes can now fly ten thousand miles without stopping. Even so, attack by air bombers is more efficient and economical when the distance flown is not great. Bombers on these very long flights need protection. The fighter planes which protect the bombers do not have the long range of the bombers. Hence, the effectiveness of the range of the bombers is limited somewhat by the range of the fighters. It should also be noted that the slower long-distance bombers are more vulnerable to attack by antiaircraft guns operated by radar and that there is the problem of distance for rockets and missiles. The evolution of the range of rockets and of airplane speeds and distances is expected to continue, and we do not know whether in the future there will be a zone of security of finite width. But, at the present, policy-makers are likely to assume that such a zone of security should be wider than that of one border of small states.

Specifically, Russia has found in the past some safety in the great distances of her capital from the base of attacking armies. Napoleon and Hitler both bogged down in the vast stretches of Russian territory. Defense in depth has historical meaning to Russia. So, in an airplane age, Russia is likely to think of the security zone around her in terms of the principle of defense in depth. To the United States, also, the western states of Europe may be not only potential bases of attack but also part of a zone of security.

The pattern of a great central state with a zone of near-by friendly states has been discussed from the point of view of security from attack, and we have seen that the coming of the airplane will probably mean a much wider zone than would otherwise be the case. But the pattern may be looked at from the point of view of attack. The zone of influence of a great power, when seen in terms of offense, depends upon how distant the potential enemy is. If the distance is very great, the zone may extend quite far, as in the case of the distance of the United States from the Marianas. The Philippines and Greece may seem very far away to Americans looking through the glasses of the nineteenth century, but with the new lenses of the air age they are our close neighbors. In the evolving technique of aviation, then, the airplane brings zones of influence of expanding dimensions.

These expanding zones of influence may be thought of as great circles measured by radii from the centers of the great powers, although history and geography do not permit one to be precisely geometrical and at the same time realistic. As these radii get longer under the influence of the airplane and the other communication and transportation inventions, the great circles around the great powers will intersect. Indeed, the intersection may be said to have occurred in middle Europe at the present time.

If this pattern of military power in the air age is as outlined in the preceding paragraphs, then the effects on policy are profound. In general, they may be thought of in two classifications. One concerns the relationship in the process of affiliation between the great central power and the states in the zone of influence; the other classification is the struggle where the great circles circumscribing the potential zones of influence overlap or approach each other. Policy in either category may be accompanied by various expressions of power and of persuasion. These various policy types will not be discussed further at this place.

It should be noted, however, that this expanding regionalism, which we have referred to as great circles, proceeds unequally depending upon the type of activity, as, for instance, military or cultural. It probably expands first and fastest with military interests. This same leadership or priority of military power in expansion is noted in that empires by conquest often came before the cultural unity of so large an area could be attained in peaceful pursuits based upon peaceful contacts.

These peaceful contacts of a cultural nature between a great central state and the smaller neighbors are also increased by aviation, other things being equal. These peaceful penetrations by communication, which are slower in expanding political areas than are the military inventions making war contacts, also have the effect of expanding regionalism in those areas with collections of states not conforming to the pattern of a great state with satellites.

These peaceful contacts have to do with travel, with the transportation of letters and express, with the spread of magazines and newspapers, and with the visits of business executives. Executives can visit a branch of their business in a foreign country in, say, less than a day. Vacations of two weeks can be spent in a distant area. The publication of some United States magazines in many different countries has been made possible by the airplane. Foreign investment in Canada, Mexico, and Africa has been facilitated by aviation. Thus the peaceful penetration of one country by the nationals of another is easier. The plane furthers travel and trade and investments because of its speed, not only over long distances, but over short routes, for the cost of traveling five hundred to fifteen hundred miles is less than the costs of a journey of three thousand to five thousand miles. These interstate contacts within a region will also be furthered by the helicopter, which travels more slowly than the airplane and with not such great nonstop distances but is suited to private travel and is not dependent upon air strips for landing. The helicopter can cross boundary lines very easily, but any effect upon the use of visas and on the collection of customs is not certain.

Aircraft, therefore, offers encouragement, through military aviation and the arrangements pertaining thereto, to the affiliations between a great power and its smaller neighbors. This expanding political and military connection is also supplemented by the encouragement which aviation gives to an expanding culture area by peaceful means.

THE IDEOLOGY OF INTERNATIONALISM

The use of an invention often has an effect indirectly upon ideas. For instance, the printing press affects democracy. And the invention of the airplane would seem to have an influence upon the ideologies of internationalism and nationalism. We have already observed the impact of aviation upon the doctrine of isolationism.

We begin with the idea of nationalism, which we consider an *esprit de corps* of a modern state or nation. In attitudes of possession and power it manifests itself in sovereignty. In the fervor of war we note its expression in patriotism. Nationalism is a group egotism that is not characterized by any special concern for other nations or states or the inhabitants thereof unless it be to the advantage of the nationalism of the particular state.

On the other hand, the term "internationalism," as used by many interpreters and as we shall use it here, implies more consideration on the part of members of one state for the interests of the peoples of another state. Indeed, the concept often envisages some larger authority than a particular state—some authority based upon a collection of states and loyalty thereto. Back of internationalism is the idea that, if states continue to war with one another and suffer from the devastation, then it is better to seek safety from war in a governmental organization devoted to the welfare of all the states. The threat of war and the desire for peace force consideration of international co-operation in a federation of states. Power in such a collection of states suggests some yielding of authority or sovereignty of the member-states. The spirit of internationalism as here conceived is that of a feeling for a larger political body than that of a single state, though the implication may be that the interests of the state will be better served in the long run by internationalism.

There are, as is to be expected, many factors that cause nationalism to flourish. Not the least of these is the competition that often leads to war but that thrives also between wars. The past glory and pride in the successes of this interstate competition cause the spirit of nationalism to persist.

War, which augments nationalism, implies a conflict of interests, that is, of interests of each of the warring groups. Thus awareness of common interests over an area is basic to nationalism. But, for a people to be aware of common interests, there must be contacts. Contact inventions, then, are the means of interests becoming common to an area which is larger than can be traveled by foot and also of their becoming manifested. Nationalism, to thrive well over a large area, depends upon printing presses, literacy (which makes the printing press a contact invention), schools, radios, telephones, boats, railways, and highways. The airplane is a new invention to be added to these and is important because it carries letters, printed matter, freight, and persons quickly over the long distances of modern states. Thus the airplane appears likely to be used to augment the ideology of nationalism.

But there are those who argue that the invention of the airplane will help to usher in internationalism. The argument is that the airplane is peculiarly fitted to cross the natural barriers such as high mountains, wide rivers, and large bodies of water which often separate states. Also the distances between communities in different states are greater than within a single state, and the airplane is suited to long distances. Hence, the airplane should, along with the radio, lead the way to the internationalism of a federation of states.

This formulation is only the statement that a new technological medium exists which may be suitable for making more contacts between nations and so may be used for furthering internationalism. The statement seems to be true, but nothing is said about the degree of its use and its influence for this purpose. But we conclude that the airplane is suitable for promoting in some degree the internationalistic ideology.

AVIATION

The airplane, as shown in previous paragraphs, is also suitable for promoting the nationalistic ideology. In truth, the airplane may be used for both purposes. An invention does not always determine its specific use. A knife may be used to prepare food or to kill, but some knives are more suited to the kitchen and others for killing. The airplane is suited very well to promoting internationalism between states and also for promoting nationalism in large states like Russia or in states with natural barriers like Brazil.

The contribution of aviation to the ideology of nationalism or internationalism may be quite slight. Certainly it is only one of many communication and transportation inventions and also of many social inventions that converge to produce a movement toward nationalism or toward internationalism. When the influence of an invention converges with other influences, a very good rule is then to inquire whether the converging influences fit in with a trend or operate against one.

We have made no special survey of trends in regard to nationalism and internationalism, but apparently there are movements of both types. It is a question, then, of which is stronger. It may very well be that nationalism is still on the rise in many, probably most, of the states of the world. Certainly such seems to be the case in China, in India, in the Near East, and in South America. Perhaps literacy and the communication inventions are aiding this growth of nationalism as well as the climate of war. On the other hand, in some of the small states of war-torn Europe, where there has been for a long time a high degree of literacy and widely spread contact inventions and where nationalism has already run a long course, it may be that these states would be willing to sacrifice some sovereignty in order to join in a union of states which would hold out the promise of peace. In these states the spirit of nationalism may be stationary or declining and probably not on the rise as much as in many non-European states.

The movement toward internationalism as previously defined seems slight as compared to the nationalistic feelings, except among a selected few who are active in the movement. Furthermore, peoples are probably not so aware of the common interests of a union of states as they are of the common interests of the people within a state, except perhaps as regards peace.

In view of the observation that the nationalistic trend seems much more powerful than the trend toward internationalism, we may expect the contribution of the airplane to be greater at present to nationalism. It may be that later the trend toward internationalism will grow greatly and that the nationalistic sentiments will weaken, in which case the airplane as an instrument for furthering internationalism will be more effective than now.

Regarding the influence of aviation on the ideologies of nationalism and internationalism, we note in conclusion that its influence is as a medium of contact and is only one such medium. Therefore, its influence is slight. Like so many inventions, the airplane can be used for opposite ends, such as good and bad, at the same time. While the airplane is especially suited to contacts between the peoples of different nations because of its attributes of speed and distance coverage, it is also suited to contacts of peoples within a state, particularly a large state. This is true because more people travel by plane for short or medium distances than for very long distances because of costs. Because aviation is only one of many influences bearing on the ideology of internationalism, it is desirable, if we are looking for practical effects, to view the trends of these ideologies. We think, then, that aviation may now be used more to further the ideology of nationalism than of internationalism, though such may not be the case at some future time.

CONCLUSION

The policies of states are concerned with their interests. These interests are affected by change and become critical in times of great inventions and of war and its aftermath. The airplane has produced changes in warfare, has affected the comparative strengths of states in warfare, and is likely to increase the peacetime contacts between states. It is around such changed relations that new policies are made and old ones modified.

The changed nature of war as a result of the use of air bombers has been to make weaker in war those congested states with vulnerable cities, unless their defense is strengthened. Then, too, since aviation makes possible long-distance attacks over natural barriers, there is less probability of a state living securely in isolation. The airplane, by making contacts in peacetime between states, favors trade, travel, and investment, so that the peacetime interests of states outside their borders are increased to some extent. Thus policies of isolationism give way to the influence of airplane and other contact inventions. In war, air bases outside a state's borders become important for both offense and defense. Hence arise policies as to how they may be had, especially in other sovereign states.

The air bomber and the armored tank have added their influence to that of the Industrial Revolution to widen the gap in power between large states and small ones and have together with population growth pushed two states out in front in military might. These two states, being far distant, seek security and advantages in offense by extending their influence outward to surrounding small states. Since the airplane can attack from a great distance, the surrounding zone of security becomes tiers of states. These great circles of influence as they intersect present zones of friction and battle grounds for cold wars. The interrelationships of states is furthered in peacetime by the uses of aviation for business and travel, which use, on the average, diminishes with distance. Between a large central state and smaller neighbors, the large state is more often a center of dispersal of goods and ideas; hence aviation extends its influence in this manner over the surrounding territory.

On the ideologies of nationalism and internationalism the airplane's influence is only one among many other influences and is probably slight. It is more probable that its immediate use will be to further the strong trend in many parts of the world toward nationalism. Aircraft are vehicles especially suited to international contacts, as well as contacts in a state of vast areas, and hence may be used sometime in the future to further the ideology of internationalism.

ATOMIC ENERGY AND INTERNATIONAL RELATIONS

By WILLIAM T. R. FOX

WHETHER one's standpoint be that of prediction or control, it is obvious that the bomb burst at Alamogordo in July, 1945, did not signalize just another triumph of modern technology. To this technological change there was a novel and almost unanimous reaction. From this day on, men said, as they first considered the social meaning of atomic energy, "We cannot go on playing the old game according to the same old rules." This paper deals with the effort of men on an unprecedented scale to discover in advance and in time to avoid extinction what the new rules must be.

ATOMIC INVENTIONS IN PEACE AND IN WAR

For a world at peace atomic fission would have startling but by no means novel consequences. It will one day, not very soon, bring cheap power and bring it to places now ill supplied. But the Western world has had a great deal of experience in adjusting to the social problems created by abundant and cheap mechanical energy. It will one day, and quite soon, bring through isotope research increases in the production of farm and factory and in the length of human life. These, too, are familiar problems for our culture with its dynamic technology.

If there were any demonstrable relations between rising standards of living and the maintenance of world peace, the task of contemporary statesmen would be clear. It would be to keep the world from blowing itself up during the next few decades until, with full bellies everywhere in the world, men had ceased to be quarrelsome. Unhappily, there is no assurance that the material benefits from the peacetime applications of atomic energy will in any way simplify the problem of keeping peace in the second half of the twentieth century. For a world at war, atomic energy poses new and terrifying problems. It is the war uses which call for adaptations of world political institutions on a scale and with a rapidity previously unknown to man.

War has provided a powerful stimulus to the development of all the major inventions of western European technology. In the case of the technological revolutions associated with the steam and steel complex of inventions, with the mass-communications inventions, and even with the airplane, the first steps were taken by private inventors. During the infancy of each of these new inventions, inquiring minds everywhere were free to speculate as to the social changes which would follow as it developed.

The atomic inventions, on the contrary, were carried all the way from the outermost frontiers of physical theory to practical application by an organization of intellectual and physical resources on a scale possible only for the government of an industrially advanced and powerful state. Furthermore, the development took place under a mantle of the most carefully preserved secrecy. In this state-sponsored development under military auspices barriers were erected to the free interchange of ideas between scientists working in various countries, even those allied with each other in destroying the Axis.[1] These were not the only barriers to free interchange of ideas among scientists, for the principle of compartmentalization in security regulations has prevented all but a trusted few from seeing the atomic-energy development as a whole. Detailed knowledge of this momentous technological advance was thus denied not only to foreigners and foreign governments but even to most of those who contributed to the advance.

The events of Hiroshima and Nagasaki tore the veil of secrecy from the fact of successful development. It also unsealed the lips of participants in the development in so far as they wished to speak on the social aspects of atomic energy. These participants had been living with a secret of momentous social import. They were not slow in dramatizing the issues of public policy posed by the new invention. Among those in the Western world who paused to reflect at all, sentiment was practically unanimous that the new atomic weapons would have to be brought under international control.[2] There was less agreement as to ways and means of bringing about the universally desired objective. Also, as it turned out, the will to achieve effective

1. It was not only free interchange between Soviet and American scientists which was interdicted but also the previously intimate relationships among the scientists of the various English-speaking countries. Thus Professor M. L. E. Oliphant writes concerning the organization of the Manhattan Project: "One immediate result of the new direction of the project, formerly managed by the Office of Scientific Research and Development, was the complete severance of contact with the British workers" (*Atomic Energy: Its International Implications* [London: Royal Institute of International Affairs, 1948], p. 38).

2. See *Bulletin of the Atomic Scientists*, Vol. I (1945–46), *passim*, for the range of official and nonofficial pronouncements supporting international control.

international control was not so evenly distributed among the governing groups of the states indispensable to a control agreement as to provide a basis for early international agreement.

Had the bomb not been developed in time for use against Japan or had it for policy reasons been developed but not used in the recent war, the military potentialities of the new weapon would have been no different from what they are now; but public reactions to the announcement of success in releasing atomic energy, if indeed there had been any announcement, would have been far less excited. First efforts at control were motivated by a sense of urgency which only the actual disasters at Hiroshima and Nagasaki could have made widespread.

The sense of urgency, based on the belief that basic political institutions would have to be altered, and altered quickly, was heightened by the activities of scientists who were not only anxious to take the lead in forming opinion but were impelled to do so by the rise of a new cult of science. The "long hairs" had "gone and done it." They were, in the public mind, if not supermen at least superbrains. Some reflected prestige of the scientists as scientists fell on them as citizens, and their political advice was widely sought and widely respected.

Because in the long period of secrecy, scientists in the Manhattan District had been able to talk with each other and only with each other, those who spoke in public, once it became possible to do so, were remarkably in agreement. The absolute weapon, they said, demanded an absolute solution. It was "one world or none." A volume of that name was published with its subtitle, "A Report to the Public on the Full Meaning of the Atomic Bomb."[3] Either there was to be a leaping development in political organization to match the leaping development in technology or there was to be a leap into the abyss and an end to the experiment called civilization. It is paradoxically true that the most urgent problems are frequently those which prove most refractory, those which do not yield on first inspection a complete solution.

The social scientist attempting to prescribe a course of action found himself caught in a dilemma. He could agree with the scientists as to the minimum necessary adaptation of world political institutions if the prospect of two-way atomic war is to be kept to a mini-

3. Dexter Masters and Katherine Way (eds.), *One World or None* (New York: McGraw-Hill Book Co., 1946).

mum, or he could point to the maximum political adaptation that could be expected, given the prevailing world political situation. But if he publicly declared that the maximum possible was less than the atomic scientists' minimum necessary, he did so at his peril.[4] His position was a little like that of the trained fire-fighter watching a brush fire creeping toward an ammunition dump which was not protected by modern fire-fighting equipment. In the long run what was needed was a modern fire engine; in the short run what was available was an old-fashioned bucket brigade. The brush fire has not been put out and the taxpayers have not agreed to buy the new engine; they have not even organized the bucket brigade.

The social scientist, whether predicting the social consequences of atomic energy or clarifying alternatives for the control of the new phenomenon, has operated under an unparalleled set of disadvantages. He is called upon to make statements about the future when (1) there is no comparable historical experience with other inventions and practically no experience at all with atomic inventions; (2) there is no peacetime application preceding the wartime application so that he may become acquainted with the inventions; and (3) there are security obstacles so great that the atomic scientist upon whom he must depend for facts, whose own knowledge is ordinarily limited by the principle of compartmentalization, is frequently not in a position to indicate the limits of his own exact knowledge.

One must assume that remaining "top secret" information would not if revealed greatly alter the analysis of the political and social consequences of atomic energy or prescriptions for adjusting to these consequences or forestalling them. It is not necessary, for example, to know how many bombs the United States now has or will have, so long as one's analysis is not based on a false assumption as to the magnitude of the stock pile. On the other hand, had it proved feasible to denature plutonium so thoroughly that there was no risk of its being "re-natured," political and social analysis based on the opposite assumption would have had to be radically revised. Or, again, this analysis assumes that it is only a question of a decade or two at most until, in the absence of international control, the Russians too

4. See, e.g., Robert M. Hutchins, *New York Times*, June 9, 1946, Book Review Section, p. 6, for a review of *The Absolute Weapon*, edited by Bernard Brodie (New York: Harcourt, Brace & Co., 1946), for a colorful indictment of social scientists who reach socially unacceptable conclusions. The volume under attack, in the writing of which the present author was a collaborator, was an early effort to apply the analytical skills of political science to the problems of atomic energy.

have bombs in significant or decisive quantities. But it is conceivable that uranium resources for fission products are so scarce and so largely within the zone of American political predominance, and the possibilities of breeding small amounts of uranium with large amounts of thorium so slight, that Russian bomb production will for a very long time remain small, however great may be the diffusion of knowledge regarding atomic-energy release. With these caveats entered into the record, one may now turn to examine the world in which fission first takes place.

THE WORLD OF THE ATOMIC BOMB

Two great power constellations dominate the world in which atomic energy is first successfully released. These two in alliance are just completing the liquidation of a third great power constellation. Had Hitler surrendered before his country had been completely devastated by air bombardments, the victorious two might have carried their wartime collaboration into the peace period, for they might have calculated on the necessity at some future date of putting down a resurgent Germany.

As it is, the two combinations have turned out to be polar opposites. They differ markedly in their methods on internal organization. The Eastern colossus consists of a mighty Soviet nucleus surrounded by a band of states with "friendly" regimes which dance attendance on Moscow; friendliness is, of course, a criterion to be defined in Moscow and separately for each regime.

Within the Soviet Union proper that country's stern rulers, with the apparent active support of most of its people, are willing to see almost every other human value sacrificed to secure the absolute security of the Soviet fortress. Such total security the leaders cannot see in any pattern of accommodation with the West. For them the conception of balance is only that of uneasy truce, subject to change without notice. Only the unanimity principle, called "the veto" on this side of the Iron Curtain, provides for them any satisfactory basis for co-operative action in the postwar world; for it leaves the Soviet leadership free to call a halt at any point.

The Western constellation of power is more loosely organized. Unified action in the West does not depend upon, and would in fact be hindered by, too blatant dictation from Washington. At its center is a state with apparently inexhaustible human and material resources. Its leaders and people at the end of the war wanted above all to get back to what they regarded as the main business of living.

It is a measure of the spontaneous and voluntary nature of collaboration among the Western powers that by no word or deed have responsible officials in Britain, Canada, or any other Western state without bombs suggested that American bombs would under any conceivable set of circumstances be used against them. They have in fact acted very much as if American bombs were their bombs.

In one way the main current of American public opinion may be running in a direction different from that in western Europe. Their own historical experience has taught Europeans to believe that international politics is a dirty business and that it will be with us a long time. To the American who wants to get back to the main business of living—including the long-deferred purchase of a new automobile, a new refrigerator, and a new home of his own, and, for many of the ex-G.I.'s, the acquisition of a new wife and some new children— European politics is a dirty business which he wants to see cleaned up in short order so that he may pursue other values not so intimately associated with state security. In 1945 he wanted to see the main line of the peace settlement laid down promptly; he wanted to see the United Nations made to work so effectively, with police force and without veto, that nobody would any longer have to play power politics; or he wanted to forget about the rest of the world.

With the invention of atomic energy two new possibilities presented themselves for avoiding the prolonged and painful business of coexisting with a not particularly friendly power constellation whose base is in Eurasia. The first was to create "One World" and to create it in a hurry. The other was simply to rub out the offending Soviet power. We need not pause at this point to inquire whether "One World" could in fact be created even if the American people and the Soviet people both willed it[5] or whether with atomic weapons Soviet power would in a thirty-minute war simply be erased. Those who want an absolute solution for the problem of the absolute weapon sometimes assume that, with Soviet rejection of the proffer of "One World," the United States is freed of any moral compulsion to seek a basis for coexistence through protracted negotiations leading to voluntary agreements on each of the host of problems disturbing Soviet-

5. Jacob Viner, "The Implications of the Atomic Bomb for International Relations," *Proceedings of the American Philosophical Society*, XC, No. 1 (January 29, 1946), 56, suggests that both the United States and the Soviet Union would have to be broken up if "One World" is to be created. He believes each is too big to be a proper member of a world federation.

American good relations. Nevertheless, the problem of American foreign policy is not ordinarily considered one of finding a moral pretext for destroying Soviet power. Presumably, the problem is still to find a basis for peaceful coexistence.

Any expectation that Soviet Russia would sign on as a charter member of "One World" has steadily diminished. It was perhaps never very high, for the polar opposites in postwar world politics differ in another way which makes difficult international agreement on any fundamental change in basic world political institutions as a means of avoiding atomic war.

One of them has sought to seal itself off hermetically against any but high-level official contact with the other. Apart from diplomats, accredited journalists, and specially invited guests being given the vodka tour, the number of American citizens who have visited the Soviet Union since the war is not far from zero. Not even Nazi Germany on the eve of the attack on Poland so effectively isolated itself. The sad fact is that UNESCO, in spite of all the brave words which have been said about it, is busy promoting educational, scientific, and cultural co-operation precisely between those peoples between whom the person-to-person contacts already existed, and in almost exact proportion to the extent that such contacts already existed. Neither its action nor any other international action has had any effect of the slightest significance in opening up this closely guarded country.

The close surveillance which the Soviet government maintains and apparently means to maintain over its citizens' contacts with the outside world makes that government peculiarly reluctant to accept such close inspection that other powers would take the risk of all-round disarmament. More grave is the real doubt that the Soviet regime is inspectable, however anxious its leaders may be to admit the principle of international inspection. This latter thought need not detain us, for the point is academic until the will to permit thoroughgoing inspection becomes manifest.

The American position on atomic disarmament is in sharp contrast to that of historic possessors of new weapons; but it is a logical position, given American foreign policy objectives and an open society whose foundations would not be threatened by external inspection. Historically, it has been the technologically backward powers which have sought by qualitative disarmament to bring a potential opponent's military technology down to their own level. The Soviet Union has, it is true, called for the outlawry of atomic weapons, but it is certainly the United States which has taken the lead in proposals to make the outlawry effective.

On conventional armaments the United States position corresponds to the position traditionally associated with technologically advanced powers. The American contention is that the powers whose chief strength lies in raw manpower must scale themselves down militarily along with the powers which depend upon small armed forces and high technology. The United States makes no similar claim with respect to atomic weapons or any of the other mass instruments of destruction. Why this is so deserves consideration, for it helps one to understand the new power equilibrium in the era of American atomic monopoly and in the era which must one day follow.

The atomic weapon is not an all-purpose instrument. If American purposes are not those which the use of atomic weapons would aid in achieving, the United States position would be improved if no power had those weapons at its disposal. In a world in which other powers possess or are expected to possess atomic weapons, an American stock pile of bombs has an important political function to discourage the use of bombs against the United States. In a world in which no other power has atomic weapons or any prospect of acquiring them, the foreign policy objectives which this country will wish to forward by using or threatening to use or even possessing such weapons are few indeed. In this latter world the American people, in terms of their own values, make no sacrifice in surrendering their present lead in the atomic armaments race.

PEACEFUL BUT NOT CORDIAL COEXISTENCE

It has from the beginning been clear that success in the quest for international control depends, first, upon the willingness of the United States to agree to weapon parity with the Soviet Union at some future date and, second, upon the establishment of generally good relations between the two giant powers. The postwar collaboration which during the war had to be assumed was seen after the war as having first to be achieved.

Whether a general settlement of issues growing out of World War II would clear the ground for international action to banish the menace of two-way atomic war cannot be known. What does seem certain is that progress toward atomic-energy control must wait upon progress in breaking the present general Soviet-American deadlock.

Whether the American bomb monopoly interfered with the general peace settlement cannot be known either. It is possible that embittered Red-haters and Russophobes have been given by the combination of the American bomb monopoly and postwar Soviet political behavior an opportunity to utter the words "preventive war." Certainly preventive war would not otherwise often be suggested as a formula for dealing with the Russians and would not be now if Americans did not find the prospect of prolonged tension almost intolerable.

There is a more important way in which the introduction of atomic weapons may have affected adversely the prospect of amicable accommodation with the Soviet Union. It has permitted the rise of a new kind of isolationism. It is easier, says the latter-day isolationist, to hit the octupus in the eye than to cut off his tentacles one at a time. It is impossible, he continues, to hold the rimlands of Europe and Asia in a new war anyhow. It is better to conserve the national energy for the main effort than to fritter it away in what will in another world war turn out to have been meaningless activity. Shoring up the sagging political structure of the European periphery is, he concludes, useless from a military point of view. This argument may be valid only for a society whose members have only a single allegiance, the United States, and only a single value, preservation of the physical security of the American continental homeland; but it is defective under any other condition.

The decision to undertake a European Recovery Program shows that the neo-isolationist concept of national policy is not yet dominant. So does the widespread support for the President's desire to strengthen the Brussels Pact with American military aid. The large number of congressmen who look benevolently on every effort to expand the air forces and seize every excuse to delay action on peacetime selective service and universal military training shows, on the other hand, how attractive the new isolationist philosophy is.

What are the prospects for peace during the period of the American monopoly? The European Recovery Program and prospective military support for the states of western Europe paid a first dividend in the form of the Communist defeat in the Italian elections of April 18 and 19, 1948. Whatever incentive Soviet leadership may have had to prolong the diplomatic deadlock, on the ground that time was on its side, was shown by that election to be disappearing. The Soviet government is more likely to seek to break the deadlock in 1949 if 1950 and 1951 would find the American position strengthened. Will it seek to break the deadlock by a return to the bargaining table or by general war or by something in between?

The American monopoly in atomic weapons furnishes part of the answer. Atomic energy was developed in that one of the power constellations which had the greater power potential.[6] Although it is widely hailed as a new *source* of energy, the energy which has so far been expended on the manufacture of fission products has certainly been far greater than the energy produced. We may say, therefore, that its importance lies in its form. It is available for special uses for which previously known forms of power were unavailable. Via atomic fission, slowly accumulated energy reserves may be suddenly released in amounts hitherto unimagined.

It is therefore no accident that the country with the greatest energy reserves developed atomic weapons. The miracle is that it did it while also prosecuting a full-scale world war. The Soviet tortoise which had thought itself gaining ground on the American hare suddenly found that the hare had leaped on; and there was still another slow, painful ascent to make before he would draw abreast of the hare.

Such equilibrium as exists between the two great power constellations rests on a more complete mobilization of power on the Soviet side and an incomparably greater power potential on the American. The outcome of any struggle between the two, whether or not within the framework of peace, depends upon where the struggle is being carried on and over what and upon the intensity of purpose displayed by each of the contenders. The line which divides the zones of predominant Soviet and Western influence varies as to location and sharpness. It is widely believed that Soviet military power could initially drive American forces out of the whole of western Europe; it is not so generally believed that the Soviet Union would emerge the victor in a third World War in which the whole of the West backed up by the American bomb monopoly was allied against it.

Publicly Soviet leaders profess to believe that the political importance of atomic bombs has been exaggerated.[7] Privately, they must

6. Energy resources, not uranium, determined the location of atomic-energy installations. On the priority of energy resources and productivity as power indexes see the chapter above (pp. 58–85) by A. P. Usher, "The Steam and Steel Complex and International Relations."

7. Edward Shils has pointed out that American leadership may also be minimizing the political importance of atomic weapons. He cites (*Bulletin of the Atomic Scientists*, September, 1947, p. 238) the article by "X" (usually attributed to George Kennan, head of the Department of State's Policy Planning Committee) which appeared in the July, 1947, issue of *Foreign Affairs*. This semiauthoritative exposition of the basis of American policy toward the Soviet Union fails to mention atomic energy.

be anxious to avoid atomic war, especially during the period of American monopoly.

Half-war or indirect war, such as the Soviet Union and the United States are now engaging in in Greece, will no doubt continue so long as unfriendly relations and a *mutual* disinclination to fight total war both persist. So will the rigorous use of economic and propaganda instruments in the battle for support in the in-between world. Atomic weapons are useless in half-war and "cold war" except in so far as they prevent the development of total war and hot war. Only by being able to support its position in half-war and in cold war will the United States be able to drive the Soviet Union back to the third alternative, a return to the bargaining table and a settlement of the diplomatic issues growing out of the second World War. A fresh assault on the problem of the international control of atomic weapons would then become possible.

Is the United States also disinclined to let half-war grow into total war? Only a widespread conviction that one-way atomic war sooner is the sole alternative to two-way atomic war later would permit United States action to bring about full-scale war. Any policy which offers the possibility of a Soviet return to a diplomacy of conciliation will almost automatically deflate any pressure for a preventive war.

The pessimistic prognosis of inevitable war assumes one of two things, neither of which is necessarily true. Either it is assumed that a two-power world will be even less stable than the multi-power world which preceded it and which has had recurring wars; or it is assumed that a two-power world can operate peacefully only if neither power is determined to dominate the world.

There may in fact be a basis for peaceful, though perhaps not cordial, coexistence in a two-power world in which one of the two has an unlimited appetite for expansion or is experiencing such insecurity that it finds no basis for satisfactory balance. If the power with the greater margin of unmobilized resources is a power which is pursuing a "live and let live" policy, then, no matter how unlimited the demands of the second power, the first power would always be in a position to mobilize to just the extent necessary to thwart the second power's designs for expansion.

Mobilization "to just the extent necessary" will, however, require more than atomic arms. As Bernard Brodie pointed out, "an American task force operating in the Mediterranean may have a stabilizing influence in the area which a strategic bombing force situated in

Utah could not possibly have—regardless of the ultimate relative effectiveness of the two types of forces in actual war."[8] With the new equilibrium resting on presence of scruple (or lack of determination) on one side and lack of weapons on the other a paradoxical conclusion emerges. The atomic-energy inventions seem to be intensifying resort to precisely those types of political competition for which atomic weapons are least useful. To avoid war in such a world situation will require that the power of great potential keep itself prepared to take all measures short of general war.

DEFENSE POLICIES IN THE MONOPOLY PERIOD AND AFTER

Whatever form the political competition takes, the polarization of power will keep pace.[9] Even if American policy succeeds in re-creating an independent western Europe capable of adopting a common line of action against the pressure from the east, the result is likely to be an increasingly clean-cut division of the world into two spheres.

So long as atomic weapons are few in number, it will be important to the Soviet Union to force these few to be delivered from the greatest possible distance. Similarly, for many years after the Soviet Union has bombs, the significance of the number which it does have can be much reduced if the United States assures itself that the use of near-by bases is denied to Soviet planes. Thus, atomic defense policy is likely to reinforce the trend toward polarization and to focus world politics on ways of winning friends and influencing people in the in-between world.[10]

As for the long-run relationships between great powers and small powers, opposing views have been developed. One thesis is that, when

8. Bernard Brodie, "U.S. Navy Thinking on the Atomic Bomb," *The Atomic Bomb and the Armed Services* (Library of Congress, Legislative Reference Service, Public Affairs Bulletin, No. 55 [Washington, 1947]), p. 26.

9. Measurement of this polarization is likely to be difficult. The Soviet colossus, with its twin engines of influence—the party, with its international connections and tactics for expansion by indirect aggression, and the state apparatus, with its armed forces—has little incentive to destroy the legal fiction of the sovereignty of its small neighbors. The American colossus is determined to maintain the sovereignty of the states of western Europe. Thus the expanded security zones of the two giant powers are unlikely to show on any map as expanded areas of government.

10. The conclusions reached above regarding the limited utility of atomic weapons, the increasing emphasis on cold war and indirect war, and the polarization of politics suggest that atomic energy has only reinforced trends which Quincy Wright declared to be dominant on the eve of the second World War. He wrote: "Modern military technique has centralized world-power in the few governments utilizing it most efficiently, has made war suicidal among these governments, has diminished the role of strictly military activity in war, and has augmented the nuisance value of war threats as an aid to the diplomacy of unscrupulous governments" (*A Study of War* [Chicago: University of Chicago Press, 1942], I, 321).

the dozen or fifteen powers with an industrial base broad enough to support a primary plutonium plant possess atomic weapons, there will no longer be any giant powers and pygmy powers. There will only be those which do and those which do not have atomic weapons. Another thesis, and probably a more accurate one, is that the genuinely independent small power with a few bombs would find that the bombs have little "blackmail" value. A few countries, like Sweden or Switzerland, with a determination to remain neutral, might, on the other hand, find respect for their neutrality strengthened.

Smaller industrial powers wholly within the security zones of the Eastern and Western giants might find that their possession of atomic weapons did not matter very much. The emphasis in Britain on the supreme need for fission products as energy sources and Canada's public declaration that atomic weapons production is beyond her resources show the reliance of both on the American stock pile.[11] Russia could not stop British and Canadian development, and the United States apparently will not. Any development behind the Iron Curtain would have the same political implications whether it occurred in Prague or in Stalingrad.

Thus, in the absence of international control, there are really only two important contingencies—monopoly and duopoly. Atomic energy may have outmoded pre-Hiroshima government areas only to introduce a new area of political control larger than the national state but not yet world wide.

Whether or not a reliable system of international control is created, an enlargement of the scope of state activity will be necessary if democratically organized states are to reduce their vulnerability to atomic attack. No great state, with or without international control, nor any world government, can afford to adhere to a political and industrial organization which would permit a complete paralysis of government to occur as a result of the successful delivery of a few bombs to key targets in such areas as Washington, New York, and Pittsburgh. In fact, the prospect for successful control would be much improved by having some of the most obvious targets made a little more difficult to destroy. It would give the control plan a margin of permissible inefficiency. A modest and sensible program of decentralization would assure the failure of a sneak attack based on

11. See N. F. Mott, "International Control: The Choice before This Country," *Bulletin of the Atomic Scientists*, III, No. 11 (November, 1947), 318, and G. C. Lawrence, "Canada's Participation in Atomic Energy Development," *Bulletin of the Atomic Scientists*, III, No. 11 (November, 1947), 328.

the illicit production or diversion of material for a few bombs. In the absence of international control it would also assure the failure of a sneak attack based on the uncontrolled production of a relatively small number. Thus, this kind of national action to reduce vulnerability will support international control if it is established; if, on the other hand, control is not established, it will prolong the period during which the United States can have security based on effective monopoly and, if it chooses, continue to negotiate for international control.[12]

Also of equal deterrent value to a power contemplating a sneak attack with a few bombs would be for its prospective victim to have many bombs with which to make a devastating retaliation. There are other ways too in which national policy can reduce the attractiveness of atomic attack by preparing in advance a wholly unwelcome counterblow. It has been pointed out, for example, that Soviet development of rocket warfare can render the British Isles a hostage to United States good behavior. Furthermore, elaborate advance planning to maintain the striking power of military units, even though the base of central direction may have disappeared, will further reduce the opportunity for cheap and successful atomic aggression.

Even in the period of American monopoly, United States defense policy will be dominated by considerations of American security during a later post-monopoly period. Already the accent in defense policy is on preparedness before the moment of supreme crisis rather than on mobilization after. With this shift of emphasis we may say that the last insular power has disappeared from world politics.

The radical expansion in state activity inherent in any adaptation to the atomic inventions is perhaps best symbolized by the nearly unanimous passage of the Atomic Energy Act of 1946 (the so-called McMahon Act). This law was passed by a conservative Congress otherwise dominated by "back-to-normalcy" motivations. The British experience with the royal navy does not suggest that that very large establishment seriously impeded the operation of normal constitutional processes. Similarly, an enormously expensive atomic-energy program, if it were sharply separated from the normal political and economic life of the nation, would not interfere with American political life; it would have as its primary domestic effect only

12. See Ansley J. Coale, *The Problem of Reducing Vulnerability to Atomic Bombs* (Princeton: Princeton University Press, 1947).

that reduction in living standards which any other not immediately productive expenditure would have.

A systematic program to reduce vulnerability by planned decentralization and by large-scale military preparedness would, however, impinge on the daily lives of citizens in many ways. As the habit of centralized decision-making became more fixed, the problem of maintaining civilian control would become more difficult. The debate over the May-Johnson Bill and its defeat in favor of the McMahon Act is only a foretaste of the problems to come.

In one way, this new emphasis on preparedness will favor a revival of a Maginot Line type of defense philosophy. The misguided experiment in fixed defenses of which M. Maginot's name is the outstanding symbol assumed that the superiority of the defense as revealed in the machine-gun technology of World War I could be maintained. It assumed that in a world of garrison states the failure of mobile warfare could be assured. Mobile warfare may be here to stay. The offense has certainly been tending to outrun the defense in so far as military technology has influenced the outcome of military engagements. Yet the day of the blitzkrieg was the day of Bismarck. Hitler almost repeated Bismarck's successes, but opposing political defenses proved in the end stronger than his initially superior military technology.

The problem of adapting society to the atomic advances in technology is the problem of finding political means, whether national or international, to improve the position of the defense. In the last year of the second World War optimistic students of world politics saw the political answer to the problem of the new technology in having a revived Europe act as a buffer between two great giants. Between the two, war would be foolish because it would be protracted and indecisive. Europe has not revived in a way to have performed this function satisfactorily even in a world without atomic weapons; but, even if it had, the atomic-energy inventions have largely destroyed the military function of the Continent as a buffer. Its mediating buffer role in a world in which neither Soviet Russia nor the United States wants a major war remains very great, however, even in the age of atomic energy.

In a new world war there would be no cushion of time if atomic weapons were available in large numbers to both of the two giant powers. There would be no lines which would have to be held for a long time until the moment for decisive action occurred. Decision in a two-way atomic war might not come early, but the most significant destruction connected with the war could come at the beginning. To reduce vulnerability to an extent which would have military significance would require that measures be completed in advance of the threat of war.

Adequate defense would not, as in the past, rest upon the resilient recuperative capacity of a productive and free but not fully prepared people. It would rest instead upon imaginative foresight in central planning and upon the fixity of purpose with which continuous preparedness is maintained in a garrison state.[13]

Satisfactory adaptation to the new technology cannot be exclusively the result of national action. It is only argued that purely national action, action not dependent on the explicit voluntary agreement of any other state, can somewhat improve the American security position. It can reduce the vulnerability of the United States to atomic attack based on possession of a few bombs, prolong the period of comparative freedom from direct attack based on its present head start, extend the period of time during which the quest for international control is able to continue, and, finally, make international control work more efficiently when and if it does come.

Neither the United States nor any other power can ever win absolute security from atomic attack by purely national action. As the period of American monopoly draws to a close and in the succeeding period as atomic armaments behind the Iron Curtain attain politically significant proportions, security not based on Soviet-American agreement will less and less seem adequate. It is this prospect which kept alive discussions in the United Nations Atomic Energy Commission, even when they appeared hopelessly stalemated. This prospect may well cause the early revival of these discussions.

Let us examine a possible trend of events if the present impasse in control negotiations persists. The American head start has depended largely upon the technological advantage and superior energy resource position which the United States already enjoyed. It has not depended upon the good fortune of having adequate uranium reserves under United States sovereignty. High United States productivity prior to Hiroshima instead explains American capacity to maintain access to the world's richest supplies in Canada and the

13. The first formulation of the garrison-state concept is to be found in articles by H. D. Lasswell. See especially "The Garrison State," *American Journal of Sociology*, XLVI, No. 4 (January, 1941), 455–68. This has since been reprinted in *The Analysis of Political Behavior: An Empirical Approach* (New York: Oxford University Press, 1948), pp. 146–57.

Belgian Congo. Advanced technology favors a much earlier complete integration of the atomic advances into the whole technology. Thus, the American lead and the security which goes with leadership are likely for a short period to grow.

There are, unfortunately, likely to be forces working in the opposite direction. The extent of Soviet uranium and thorium resources are not known, nor are the extent of energy resources known which the Soviet government could allocate to atomic-energy development without sacrificing some other critical element of industrial or military strength. One cannot assume on the basis of present publicly available data that Soviet resources are inadequate on either count. If they are adequate, only voluntary agreement or preventive war can stop Soviet bomb production. Possibly within a decade and probably within two decades, Soviet production of fissionable materials would reach what might be called the saturation point.

By "saturation point" is meant a stock pile of atomic weapons large enough to destroy the targets against which atomic weapons are peculiarly suited. The number of large cities in the world is limited, and "conventional" arms can destroy lesser targets, so that the number of large-city targets governs the saturation point. At some future date, in the absence of international control, there is likely to be more than one stock pile in the world whose size exceeds the saturation requirement. The American stock pile would be larger than any other, but the American people would be unwise to derive much comfort from that fact.

The situation might be like that which Mark Twain described of the proposed duel with axes.[14] The appetite of neither duelist for the duel was very great in a situation in which each thought both would be killed. In the less stylized form of conflict which is modern war, however, a government with no appetite whatsoever may start a conflict if its leaders feel sure that the opponent is about to start it. They may start it if they feel that the opponent has for a long time been unscrupulously trading on their own general unwillingness to start a war.

"MIDDLE-RUN" CONSIDERATIONS

Until two-way atomic war breaks out, there is always the possibility of heading it off. Plural possession of substantial stock piles of atomic weapons would make two-way atomic war a real possibility,

14. Cited by Wright, *op. cit.*, II, 799.

but plural possession does not mean the automatic and inevitable extinction of civilization. The burden of proof, however, is on the complacent if they assert that plural possession of atomic bombs offers no real threat to the future of civilization or to the security of civilized states.[15]

There is in the interval before the American atomic monopoly finally wastes away no cause for being complacent. Science and technology will not stand still. The success of the atomic scientists has dramatized the importance and expanded the budgets of research and development programs within the armed services. One previously existing obstacle to improvement in the techniques of mass destruction has been forever removed. Any fertile suggestion for mass destruction will in an age of nationalized science be investigated because there will always be the fear that the other nation's scientists might make the discovery first. Apart from motives of patriotism which animate laboratory scientists as they do other citizens, humanitarian motives will now motivate a scientist to penetrate the realms of mass destruction if only to discover how protection may be won from the new scourge. The combined effect of expanded budget and intensified motivation will be further to accelerate the rate at which military technology is changing.

Previous armaments regulation has always presupposed a relatively stable military technology. To lay down precise obligations or to calculate the political consequences of any proposed arms regulation is almost impossible when the military technology is in violent flux. Furthermore, the nation which is bargaining away its atomic ace may find that in the next deal some other nation will come up with a different ace.

A world of prospective plural bomb possession, of rapidly changing military technology, and of nationalized and uninhibited science is a new world to which man will have to make a very complex adaptation and will have to make it quickly. A mass educational program will have importance to the extent that it prepares the popular mind

15. See Harold C. Urey, "Atomic Energy, Aviation, and Society," *Air Affairs*, I, No. 1 (September, 1946), 21–29, for a jeremiad on the consequences of plural possession. If Professor Urey's gloomy forebodings cannot be confirmed by scientific demonstration, neither can they be dismissed by any scientific demonstration that they cannot be borne out by future experience. To taunt the atomic scientists by calling them "a league of frightened men" is not only an insult to their courage and integrity but a callous exhibition of blindness. The need for important political adaptations to the atomic-energy inventions is not lessened by any demonstration that a particular scientist has only a partial answer or even by a demonstration that he has a wrong answer.

for radical and carefully planned adaptations. As the Federation of American Scientists statement of December 9, 1947, declared: "What is needed now is the overpowering will to agree, the all-out effort to act, not as if one nation is the enemy of another, but with the realization that all nations are partners in the desperate enterprise of living together. It is not the mechanism of the United Nations which is at fault; in this respect the substitution of any other system would not appreciably alter the situation as long as the will to agree is absent."[16]

One would, however, be doing a disservice to the American people and to civilization in general if one interpreted this or any similar statement to mean that it is within the powers of the United States *alone* to establish world control of atomic energy. If control is to be achieved, the "overpowering will to agree" must be developed on both sides of the Iron Curtain. This necessity is not evaded by bringing forth proposals for "limited world government."[17] It would also be a disservice if it propagated the belief that any world government proposal, no matter how ill conceived, would necessarily be better than any security policy based on national action, no matter how enlightened. Finally, it would be a disservice to suggest that any plan for international control which falls short of world government is necessarily worse than no control plan at all. The will to agree must be supported by an understanding of the minimum conditions which a control plan must satisfy to be acceptable.

The discussions in the United Nations Atomic Energy Commission are for the time being suspended. This was hardly due to a failure of the American people to will international control intensely enough. In 1948 increasing lack of American confidence in Soviet good faith, which is the result of a three-year Soviet-American diplomatic impasse, may not permit international agreement along the lines of the original Acheson-Lilienthal Report. However, the White House, the leadership of the armed forces, and enlightened molders of opinion were so firmly committed to an international control plan based on an American surrender of its atomic monopoly in the year after Hiroshima that one cannot fairly attribute failure of control negotiations to a lack of public pressure to achieve control.

16. *Bulletin of the Atomic Scientists*, IV, No. 1 (January, 1948), 2.

17. "Limited world government," i.e., world federation minus the Soviet Union and its satellites, is frequently advocated as a step toward "true" world government. If there is anything to be said in favor of such a proposal, it is because it is a proposal based on organizing a preponderance of force against the Soviet Union. This is a policy which advocates of world government have generally held tantamount to planning for the extinction of the human race.

If control negotiations are ever to be revived, what the American government needs is discriminating pressure. It would be a great disaster if American negotiators felt that they had to produce some agreement, even if it were wholly along the lines of the Soviet proposals. American policy will fail if it is not based upon widespread understanding of the minimum conditions of international agreement, i.e., those conditions which if not satisfied would make an agreement worse than useless. What are some of these conditions?

The widely held proposition that world government must be created within x number of years is frequently confused with a totally different proposition—that it is useless to attempt to patch up the existing world political order. The transcontinental tourist with a flat tire in the mountains may be convinced that his spare will never get him to San Francisco; but he is still willing to put it on in the hope that it will get him down from the mountains to a point where he can purchase a new tire.

To put discriminating pressure on one's government requires a grasp of what may be called "middle-run" considerations. Belief in the long-run adequacy of this or that proposed line of action provides no basis for rejecting "middle-run" or short-run proposals for action. Overconcentration on long-run considerations may result in such complete lack of regard for questions of feasibility as to promote the war which an "adequate" long-run solution seeks to avoid. Modern civilization can, after all, only be destroyed once. If it is destroyed because methods of getting along peacefully through the next generation on the basis of voluntary agreement are rejected, the adequacy of a solution which if it had been adopted would then have given absolute security would be irrelevant.

Overconcentration on long-run considerations also ignores the beneficent possibilities which might follow the adoption of a number of ameliorating "inadequate" policies. Taken together, their effect might create a new burst of confidence in man's capacity to deal rationally with atomic energy, a new will to achieve effective control, and a new framework within which control could be negotiated.

An opposite evil is overconcentration on the short run. Those who would have maximum present security in exchange for a future of assured insecurity exhibit this defect in their thinking. Another manifestation of overconcentration on the short run is the restless search for the tactic which will break the present diplomatic log jam. Taken in conjunction with a middle- and a long-run plan of action, the search for the one correct immediate tactic has relevance, although even in this case the professional diplomat is likely to have a better grasp of tactics than an outsider. But by itself a proposal of an immediate tactic as if it were a complete solution deserves short shrift.

An illustration is the frequently heard proposal for a personal conference between the President of the United States and Marshal Stalin. Another is the suggestion that each of these two gentlemen be given access to the nation-wide broadcasting systems of the other nation. Neither tactic can be judged apart from the steps which would have to follow. Mr. Truman would, for example, have to make a statement to Mr. Stalin or to the Soviet people. For him to make such a statement he would have to have a program of action to present as a basis for negotiation. This program would involve considerations of policy over the next few years, and it is the program of action rather than the proposal for a Truman-Stalin meeting which requires public discussion to provide enlightened and discriminating support to the government.

This brings us to the question of the middle-run considerations which in fact govern the direction of great-power policy, including United States policy on atomic-energy control. What can in fact be done, short of setting up a true world government, which if done will make it easier to solve the remaining unsolved questions? If one can define this sphere of action, he can state what parts of the control problem are negotiable separately from the creation of a world authority with coercive power of its own such that it can coerce great states and small states and coerce them with equal effectiveness.

From the American point of view an international control plan which is not rascal-proof would be worse than no plan. Our present insecurity, in which we know we have bombs but are not sure when the other fellow will have them, would be as nothing to the insecurity of a people who had given up their bombs only to discover that the other fellow has secretly and illegally come into possession of some. The essential and therefore minimum separable portion of a total control plan would be one that gave in sufficient time reliable knowledge that no country was manufacturing or stock-piling significant quantities of illicit fissionable materials.[18] The qualification "in sufficient time" means that knowledge must come in time for preponderant force to be organized against the violator.

18. See William T. R. Fox, *The Struggle for Atomic Control* (New York: Public Affairs Committee, 1947).

The corollary which one segment of military thinking drew from this proposition about minimum control is as follows: "We appreciate that the most we can expect from a system of international atomic control is a period of approximately one year in which to prepare for a full-scale atomic attack with significant quantities of bombs after warning has been given of a major violation of international control regulations on the part of one nation or a group of nations; therefore, we must retain indefinitely, in accord with international agreements, our knowledge and industrial capacity to produce atomic weapons."[19] The War Department point of view just expressed is ambiguous as to whether any other country is to be permitted "knowledge and capacity to produce atomic weapons" in exchange for its promise not to produce them. We must assume, however, that any voluntary agreement to limit or prohibit the production of atomic weapons must put the United States and the Soviet Union on the plane of full equality in this matter.

How can the requirements of a reliable warning system and full equality between the Big Two be met? One recent development may make this task politically less difficult. So long as cheap and abundant power from atomic energy appeared an imminent possibility, there seemed no way to avoid large-scale plutonium production in peacetime. But to have permitted production of militarily significant quantities of fissionable materials would have required international agreements on quantities and ratios of permitted production.

Fortunately, the imminent peacetime applications of atomic energy in the field of isotope research do not require militarily significant amounts of fission products. The way is thus paved for preservation of strategic balance (including equality between the Big Two) on the basis of all nations surrendering their right to produce militarily significant amounts. This is the so-called "0-0-0" (zero-zero-zero) proposal.[20] So long as atomic energy remains unavailable as an efficient power source, the cost in terms of peacetime benefits of agreeing to shut down large-scale production of fissionable materials everywhere in the world would be nil even for the United States with its huge investments at Oak Ridge and Hanford.

One final word is perhaps necessary as to what an initial control

19. "The Effects of the Atomic Bomb on National Security (An Expression of War Department Thinking)," *Army and Navy Journal*, April 12, 1947; reprinted as "War Department Thinking," *Bulletin of Atomic Scientists*, III, No. 6 (June, 1947), 151.

20. See, e.g., proposal by D. F. Cavers, *Bulletin of Atomic Scientists*, III, No. 10 (October, 1947), 283.

agreement should not contain. The changed emphasis in national policy from mobilization after the crisis to preparedness before the crisis reduces the value of a token international police force in enforcing any violation of an atomic-energy control agreement. No other kind of international police force is today at all probable. Deterrent action and enforcement action will therefore have to be primarily national action. It is of great importance that this not be hampered by any requirement that it wait upon the exhaustion of the labyrinthine procedures of the United Nations. What is needed at the international level as a practical first step is a reliable fire-alarm system. The members of the present volunteer fire department must not be kept away from the scene of the fire because a professional group of fire-fighters may some day be organized.

PREVAILING BELIEFS

A convenient way of summarizing this analysis is to restate the ways in which prevailing beliefs about the necessary social adaptation to atomic-energy developments have become clearer in the thirty months of active discussion.

1. The need for planned and rapid adaptation of world political organization in the atomic era is apparent, as it has been from the first public announcement of the bombing of Hiroshima; but it is now more widely believed that the first step may have to be taken before the last step is clearly seen.

2. Soviet-American will to collaborate was assumed to exist in the field of atomic-energy control in 1945 as it was in every other field. In 1948 it is recognized that agreement depends on developing the Soviet will to agree at least as much as the American.

3. The limitations of atomic weapons as instruments of policy are more clearly seen in 1948 than in 1945. Preventive war if possible looks less attractive now than then and the utility of atomic weapons to achieve atomic-energy control may be doubted.

4. A world with no international authority to control atomic energy seemed the worst possible prospect in 1945. In 1948 it is recognized that an ineffective control plan would be worse.

5. In 1945 there was a tendency to assume that definitive solutions could be found within a relatively short time. Now there is a wider expectation of prolonged impasse and continuing irritable Soviet-American relations.

6. In 1945 the possibility of any very effective national action to

make a world of no-control tolerable was heavily discounted. Now it is being re-examined.

7. The first step toward international control is seen to be a very big step, a rascal-proof inspection plan; but the internationalization of enforcement action must follow at a later date. This first step would not banish war, but it might make it possible for the war to be concluded before atomic destruction had been wrought on all the great cities of all the participants.[21]

8. Neither total war nor total peace is inevitable, nor does this exhaust the range of possibilities. There is a third possible eventuality, protracted bad relations, ultimately perhaps followed by slow improvement.[22]

21. See Coale, *op. cit.*

22. See H. D. Lasswell, "The Interrelations of World Organization and Society," *Yale Law Journal,* LV (August, 1946), 889–909.

THE MASS-COMMUNICATIONS INVENTIONS
AND INTERNATIONAL RELATIONS

By ROBERT D. LEIGH

PRESENT knowledge regarding the interaction between inventions in mass communication and the surrounding political and social institutions in the field of international relations is rudimentary. No precise data in this area are available for our guidance so far as I know. What follows, therefore, is of the order of speculation or description of phenomena in plain view.[1]

Attention will be focused on *modern mass* communication rather than upon communication as a whole or communication over a long historical range. Mass communication here means communication which extends *immediately* beyond face-to-face contact between the two or more persons communicating. It implies for the recipients a certain disembodiment of the communicator and for the communicator an unseen audience. The elimination in our consideration of communication between persons and groups in home, neighborhood, school, lodge, theater, church, club, and union leaves out the area which up to now has been basic in the formation of opinion, prejudice, loyalty, understanding, solidarity, or divisiveness. By stressing immediacy, the definition rules out also the extension of communication in point of time through written and other repositories of man's thought and imagination: manuscripts, libraries, and museums. Thus it omits consideration of major discoveries of great social consequence such as of the symbols of written language, of papyri and paper, of the hand press, and of the transport of messages by foot courier, waterway, road, and railroad.

We may define the modern period in mass communication as signalized by the group of inventions beginning in the early nineteenth century and multiplying in the last fifty years. These inventions appear not to be independent sources of social change so much as particular manifestations of the major technological changes of the period: of power-driven machinery, of fast transport, of electric energy,

1. If the exposition given here of the acceleration and multiplication of mass-communications inventions makes clear the need for both acceleration and multiplication of governmental and independent scholarly inquiries into their social impact, the writer's effort will be rewarded.

and of optics. Conversely, the communications inventions are contributing parts of a larger technological-institutional complex having the general characteristics of urbanization, industrialization, extension of markets, and a common government over vastly extended areas.

Unlike steam, steel, aviation, and atomic energy, the modern mass-communications inventions are a cluster of more or less related things, not one thing. It will clarify our discussion to list them.

THE MAJOR MASS-COMMUNICATIONS INVENTIONS

First came the steam-driven printing press early in the nineteenth century. There followed in order the high-speed rotary press, the linotype machine, and the photo-engraving process. On them was built the city newspaper of large local circulation. After these early developments press machinery, partly because of the very large plant investment required, underwent only minor improvements and survived into the present decade with no major changes.

Just now, however, we are witness to a new series of printing-press inventions: electromatic typewriter typesetting in place of linotype or stereotype, lighter magnesium and rubber plates or elimination of copper and other metal plates entirely, and photo-offset and rotary printing for smaller book and magazine printing. It is too early to say what these experiments will lead to in publishing operations. Their promoters estimate, however, that they will cut off two-thirds or more of the investment in plant machinery for the small and middle-sized newspaper plant and that they will reduce from 50,000 to 15,000 the minimum economical run for cheap-priced books. If substantiated in practice, these economies by themselves would seem to favor more dispersed newspaper- and book-publishing units, although they are, of course, only one among several factors affecting concentration or dispersion of ownership of publishing units.

A second series of major inventions in the field of mass communication consisted of the land-line telegraph, submarine cable, and land-line telephone. These were pioneered in the mid-nineteenth century and extensively developed as point-to-point commercial or governmental services in the latter part of the nineteenth and early twentieth centuries. In recent years technical improvements in telegraph and cable transmission have been introduced, mainly increasing speed (from sixty to two hundred words per minute for cable transmission) and accelerating the volume of communication which may be carried over a single wire or cable.

A third series of inventions, appearing at the beginning of the present century, has tended to challenge, if not to replace, the cable and land-line transmission for international message traffic. These are the radio (or wireless), telegraph, and telephone. As developed commercially, the newer system retained the point-to-point principle but eliminated the cost of wire or cable between the points of transmission and reception. Because of the late development of cross-ocean telephone transmission, this radio technique is almost the sole means used by telephone networks for these great distances. During the recent war and after, the two handicaps of the newer, cheaper service (i.e., atmospheric disturbance and lack of privacy) have been largely overcome—the first by developing a network of alternative routes, making it possible to by-pass local atmospheric disturbances; the second by scrambling devices.

A fourth major mass-communications invention following radio-telegraph and telephone point-to-point was that of radio broadcasting to carry sound, whether voice or music, from a central point to private receiving sets anywhere within a large radius. Pioneered as early as 1910, radio broadcasting came with a rush at the end of the first World War. By the mid-twenties the shorter waves were being used for broadcasts over long distances. By the thirties broadcasting had a range which spanned continents and oceans.

A fifth major invention was the motion picture. Preceded by a decade of experiment and commercial beginnings, movies became industries, with their own production, distribution, and exhibition houses in the first decade of the twentieth century. The use of sound with motion pictures began in the late twenties, and color was added in the thirties, to make the contemporary entertainment picture presentation. During the period between the wars there was a less obtrusive expansion of range of the film medium to include the animated chart and cartoon, the visual editorial or documentary film, and nonfiction narrative.

Sixth is a cluster of inventions, all recent and some still in the experimental stage, which combine elements of the newspaper press, radiotelegraph, radio broadcasting, the typewriter, and photography.

One is the facsimile transmission process by which whole pages of text or photographs, or both, and in color, are sent by wireless on a point-to-point basis. Another is the multiple-address system of transmission which involves sending dot-dash and/or facsimile material by wireless from one point simultaneously to many other points in a large region, the receiving points usually being newspapers licensed to receive the material for their use. Multiple address cuts the cost of transmission of voluminous news material as much as ten times under relayed point-to-point transmission. Still another adaptation of the radio facsimile process is its use to transmit a newspaper from the newspaper office direct to home receivers. As yet still in an experimental stage, the radio newspaper, as it is called, possesses the potential advantage of eliminating power presses, newsstands, newsdealers, and trucks, trains, and airplanes for distribution. Organized as a chain of stations, the daily radio newspaper might be distributed simultaneously over much larger areas than is now possible. Another adaptation is the teletypewriter mechanism for sending and reception of messages. This provides a simple typewriter-key transmission and automatic typed, noncode recording at the receiving end. It is used for multiple-address transmissions or back-and-forth communication by telegraph line or wireless between business, government, or news offices and agencies. And from the recent war, where it was developed as a mechanism for tactical communication, has come the "walkie-talkie" radio which enables both transmitter and receiver of radio communication to be on the move rather than at fixed spots.

A seventh major invention is television, now just beginning to pass out of its experimental phase into commercial use. With television, mass communications turns almost the full circle—back to something approximating face-to-face discourse. For in television eventually the ongoing event in full motion, color, and sound is brought directly to the person in his home (or cocktail bar) but from great distances far beyond his normal reach of eye and ear. In one sense, a combination of radio and motion picture, television promises to be different from both.

Along with the battery of inventions using electric impulses for transmission has come a new range and a new speed for print and film through the development of air mail and express transport on a global scale. The most far-reaching network for mass communication still is the system of national post offices. A business rather than a mechanical invention, albeit made not by business organizers but by a British civil servant in the nineteenth century, the "penny post" provides within each country a uniform low rate for long and short hauls, a near equality of service for city and country dweller, a simple, single, cheap system of communication of letters, magazines, pamphlets, and books. By reciprocal agreement between national governmental monopolies there is, furthermore, an articulated network of nondiscriminatory private communication, freer from censorship than other means of mass communication, generally and fully accessible to all, from anywhere to anywhere on the globe.

With the development of air transport on a large scale, films, magazines and books, light plastic magazine mats ready for separate publication, and manuscript copy for newspaper, magazine, or book can be distributed from one point to another, so that widely separated, simultaneous publication of material in many languages is a practical possibility. Thus the postal network is both a separate means of mass communication and a means for the extension in range of the other mass media.

MASS-COMMUNICATIONS INVENTIONS AND SOCIAL INSTITUTIONS

The foregoing description of the developments in mass communication during the last hundred years and more reveals three obvious facts of social significance. First is the multiplication and acceleration of types of mass media of communication; second, the increasing reach of the newer media; third, their increasing richness.

Multiplication.—Until well into the nineteenth century we had as almost the sole means of large-scale, public communication the hand press. It was able to produce, slowly and at large unit cost, printed products limited by necessity to a small percentage of the population. But in rapid succession there appeared not only power printing presses, turning out newspapers, pamphlets, magazines, and books much more rapidly and more cheaply than before, but also printed photographs and print in color; wired and wireless message networks, latterly expanded into means for the rapid sending of pages in full text and color as well as broadcasting speeches, drama, music, and what have you; the moving—then moving and talking—picture; and now television, the radio-transmitted moving and talking picture, which provides a fireside seat for distant events as they happen. In the field of communication this is a rate and volume of invention fully equal to the changes in the use of nonhuman power for driving machinery which we call the Industrial Revolution.

Enlargement of area.—A review of the list of communications inventions reveals with equal clarity their enlargement of the area of mass discourse. Here, technical possibilities far outrun present commercial and governmental operations. The technical machinery available or in blueprint could provide daily or hourly newspapers delivered by radio to all the homes of a continental state; it could transport films or magazine scripts and plates in the space of a week around the world; by radio point-to-point network it could tie agencies and outposts in different continents into quick back-and-forth personal communication; by a relay network it could broadcast a single speaker so that he would reach all who may listen around the globe; and even now man anywhere can put his thoughts or wishes on paper, seal them, post them in a box, and have assurance that a friend or business firm halfway round the world will receive them in a matter of a week or two.

Increase of richness.—A third characteristic of the century's development in mass communication is the increase of fulness and richness of the content which can readily be distributed over great areas. Until twenty-five years ago long-distance communication was in the form of the dot-dash signals of international Morse code or in the form of *cold* print. Now there can be sent over great areas the warmth and color of drama and combat re-enacted; the fulness of a public event seen from the balcony; the ordered picture of the background of events illustrated by chart, diagram, and sample incident.

Larger units of control.—Less surely, a fourth general deduction may be made regarding the modern communication inventions. This is that, as the range of the media develops, the units of management or control become fewer. There are some exceptions to this tendency. As has been noted above, possibly the printing inventions now appearing may appreciably reduce the plant investment required for a modern urban newspaper and help to reverse the trend toward city newspaper consolidation generally assumed to be a result of the heavy cost of printing machinery. But if the facsimile newspaper should appear, it could be extended to a national audience only by the creation of connecting transmission stations covering each horizon range (at least at the present stage of the radio art). And this means some central supervision. It should be noted also regarding the sources of news whether distributed by small or large units that there are only three major news agencies providing the more than seventeen hundred daily newspapers with their news other than local.

As rapid air transport becomes fully reliable for the fast distribution of radio transcriptions, widely separated and owned radio stations could operate without networks. It should be pointed out, however, that the system of widely dispersed radio-station ownership in the United States is the product of federal statute and administrative license, not of economic forces. And for international broadcasting, the United States government operates as a single unit, with arrangements for limited private-company participation only. Most other countries operate radio broadcasting, especially network broadcasting, as a national monopoly.

The high production costs of television and the necessity for networks or chains for distribution of televised programs seem to argue for centralized controls of this important new medium. Cable, wire, and wireless companies to handle commercial messages have been built as government-owned or government-related monopolies in most countries, and in others (i.e., South America) two or three huge foreign companies operate the service within their borders. In the United States we now have a domestic telephone near-monopoly, a domestic telegraph monopoly, with two other companies only (one a large investor in foreign domestic telecommunication systems, the other the owner of one of the four domestic radio broadcast networks) sharing with them most of the international telecommunications business. Such economic analysis of the industry as has been made suggests merger rather than more competitive units as the sounder trend.

The motion-picture business of the United States has grown into a closely integrated system dominated by eight giant Hollywood companies. And for purposes of foreign export these major companies are organizing single corporations for each important national market.

It is no accident, probably, that the most highly articulated system of international communication, that operating under the International Postal Convention of 1875, represents a co-operative arrangement between national postal monopolies.

On balance, then, modern mass communication as it grows in extent seems to move almost inevitably toward larger and fewer units.

This runs counter to a firmly held tradition in the United States and some other Western countries not only that freedom of communication is a major requirement for social health and progress but that the freedom of the communication depends upon widely distributed and unregulated ownership of the originating centers of publication and programming. The stubborn fact of "large-scaleism" which seems to inhere in modern mass communication thus suggests a conflict between these opposing forces of technological requirement and social tradition. The resolution of the conflict may be in one of three directions: (*a*) a decline of actual freedom, (*b*) legal prohibitions against large units of controls, or (*c*) a gradual organization of large-scale units, by law or custom, so that freedom of expression, debate, and dissent operates within the larger structure. The last would seem to be the most sensible direction in which to go. But one should avoid making the assumption that the technical advantage of, and pressure for, large-scale controls will triumph over firmly imbedded cultural habits.

MASS MEDIA AS INSTRUMENTS OF NATIONALISM-IMPERIALISM

What of the social significance of the multiplication, the extending reach, the increasing richness, and the larger units of control of modern mass communication? My primary assumption is that, because the newer media loom so large in the common life, they will play an increasingly important part in the making and changing of the loyalties, prejudices, attitudes, judgment, and understanding of people everywhere. They are becoming, in short, a major, potential instrument for conscious, directed (or for undirected, random) social change. What these changes might be is a matter of control and direction of the instruments. The instruments themselves are neutral.

As operated up to the present—and it must be recalled that the cable, telegraph, wireless, and motion picture took their shape in an age of nationalism, imperialism, and war—the media have been directed largely to serve business, governmental, and social interests within national states and to consolidate nationalist and imperialist loyalties and sentiments.

During the early part of the period Great Britain was the leading power. Not only was London the world's center of commerce and finance; it was its predominant center of communication. And the British communications instruments were organized on an imperial, English-language basis. The British were the earliest to grasp the importance of submarine cables and built an overseas network which by the time wireless telegraph appeared was easily the major system of international press communication for messages and press material. Great Britain took an important place also in the development of wireless telegraph after the first World War; and the two systems were united, between the wars, into a single government-aided network (Cables and Wireless) designed primarily to serve the Empire but open to others who wished to use its far-flung facilities. The central communication point through which flowed all the message traffic, however, was London. At the end of the recent war Cables and Wireless was taken over completely by the government, where it is being articulated with the British Post Office. The Post Office, on its part, during the recent war added to its domestic mail and telegraph monopoly an extensive overseas service of multiple-address wireless-press transmissions.

In radio the British developed their domestic broadcast service as a single government corporation (B.B.C.) for domestic programs, extended it in the thirties for overseas programs aimed at the Empire, and later adapted it to serve as a news service to foreign countries. In the field of books and magazines the British developed fully the English-language market throughout the Empire. So, too, by the early development (1850) of the Reuter's international press news service, a strong national-imperial feeder of material for British, Empire, and foreign newspapers was built up. Reuter's was nongovernmental in ownership but until the recent war maintained a sympathetic relation to British governmental policy.

Only in motion pictures did the British plainly lag behind other nations—a lag which in recent years they are doing their best to overcome, both by encouragement of their own production and by limitation of imports of foreign pictures.

The British communications system was thus an extremely valuable instrument for the transaction of overseas and imperial governmental, commercial, and financial affairs. It was also valuable in serving the cause of national and imperial solidarity. It would be incorrect to say that the existence of the technical instruments of modern mass communication in British hands created the Empire or held the Empire together. It would be nearer the truth to say that the Empire created the communication system or, at least, that the mass-communications system was an essential element in the imperial system. Without it the Empire would have faltered.

The British system stands as the prototype for the communications systems of the great powers up to the period preceding the second World War. All the European nations, large and medium-sized, provided themselves with a domestic telegraph and telephone network, a domestic press agency, a domestic radio broadcast system, and a considerable newspaper, magazine, and book press. The French and Dutch made heavy investments in submarine cables designed as imperial links and followed them up with overseas wireless systems.

The French developed their subsidized press agency, Havas, and for a time joined with Reuter's and Wolff of Germany in dividing the world's press agency business, taking for Havas the French Empire, southwestern Europe, North Africa, and South America. France developed its own broadcasting system also, for its home and for its empire audience. Germany entered the field of overseas communication late, with cables, a press association, a radio broadcast service, and, most successfully of all, a center of book publication for export of books both in the German and foreign languages. At the end of the first World War, however, Germany lost her cables and her press association; at the end of the second World War her broadcast system and Leipzig book center were liquidated.

Japan emerged as a world power early in the twentieth century and imitated her rivals by building her own cable and wireless network, her Domei press agency, and, later, an extensive international broadcasting system serving especially the Pacific islands and East Asia.

The development of mass communication in the United States during this period shows many points of likeness to the other major powers but some points of significant difference. We were becoming a great power, and we had some noncontiguous possessions. But for a large part of the hundred years our continental area itself was our empire and our main commercial-industrial-cultural preoccupation. Several American companies early entered the field of cable and wireless telegraph development to points in our American possessions, to near-by foreign countries, and to distant capitals overseas. None of these companies, however, was directly owned or controlled by the government (although the Navy, for strategic reasons, had a lively interest in their development).

Three American press associations were built up before the first World War to serve the domestic press and for this purpose extended their activities overseas. More latterly, they have become two-way agencies serving foreign newspapers as well as our own. From first to last, however, the press associations have maintained a militant independence from government controls. Their announced policy is that of providing an international commodity—news. They eschew any function of serving one national political purpose more than another. How far this policy serves to free these news associations from an unconscious national, cultural bias, one cannot say.

A similar situation has prevailed in motion pictures. Because of the early development of technical skills and economic strength, the

Hollywood silent movies developed leadership among the world's motion-picture industries. Hollywood sought and gained a large share of the foreign markets. With the advent of sound in motion pictures there was some setback in non-English-speaking countries. But by the time of the outbreak of the second World War our films still led all other countries in showings in the world's theaters. Without doubt, Hollywood through the film medium was familiarizing people in other lands with American life, customs, and ideas. But it was not presenting a picture that the leaders of American government or of American civic life felt was either representative or favorable. Certainly Hollywood, no more than the press associations, did not harbor any consciously nationalistic or imperialistic design.

Thus most of American pre–World War II mass communication in its international aspects, in contrast to the other great powers, seemed to represent no national policy at all. Excepting the United States, however, the principal use and probable effect of mass communication up through the first World War was to solidify and to strengthen the prevailing nationalist-imperialist temper of the time.

PROPAGANDA AND WAR—COLD AND SHOOTING

In the thirties the imperialist use of the media took on a sharper, more aggressive character. Especially were medium- and short-wave radio and the newer instrument of multiple-address wireless employed to reach groups speaking the language of the home country, or ideologically sympathetic groups living under foreign governments. The earliest of these efforts were the Russian foreign-language broadcasts in German aimed at German workers. The Hitler government in the thirties, in turn, addressed radio and other appeals to German-speaking peoples in Austria, Czechoslovakia, and South America. More quietly the Spaniards sent broadcasts to Latin America accentuating the common elements in Hispanic culture; and Japan addressed its fellow-nationals throughout Asia and on the American West Coast.

Rather rapidly this took on the aspects of a cold war in which all the available means of mass communication under direct or indirect government control were operated in the interest of a territorially aggressive or, as in the case of the British and French, a defensive policy.

With the advent of the shooting war in 1939 the mass machinery was expanded and mobilized for the task of both strategic and tactical propaganda warfare. Among the major powers the United States was obliged to improvise most of this machinery. Especially was this true of the overseas radio and multiple-address program. Indeed, the military had to build out of existing parts and new construction an independent radio telecommunications network for their purposes.[2]

The disposition of the world's mass communications equipment changed somewhat as a result of World War II. The German and the Japanese communication machinery and personnel have been destroyed or requisitioned for supervised use by the victor nations. The same is to a great extent true of Italy. France has lost its position as a leading power in the field of mass communication.

Russia, on the other hand, has maintained its mass-communications organization and activities on a cold-war footing. And Great Britain has maintained its well-developed mass-communications operations with no great changes. Indeed, in the case of motion pictures there is in Britain a postwar expansion of activity, both domestic and overseas.

The United States, on the other hand, has dissipated a large part of its war-built organization and operations for international mass communication, as it did its military and naval personnel, on the theory that the war was over. The liquidation was not complete. Some of the short-wave radio operation was continued; the private press associations and motion-picture companies have attempted to regain ground lost during the war. A single government magazine for Russia continues; and at least two large commercial publishers have built an impressive network of foreign-language editions of their American magazines tailored to meet the susceptibilities of foreign readers.

If we accept the thesis that in many respects we are engaged in a cold war for common adherence to a social cultural system shared with western Europe, the technical potential of mass communication is not unfavorably disposed so far as the United States and the western European nations are concerned. Along with Great Britain we have a major share of the world's telecommunications equipment,

2. Presumably the American military organizations have made studies of the specific usefulness of the tactical propaganda operations in the recent war. So far as I know, however, no thorough studies have been made of the effectiveness of the specific elements in our wartime strategic propaganda. The relevance of such study is that it should serve as guide not only in a program of national defense but also in a program of peacetime struggle because a sober view of the present world is that it has changed not from war to peace but from shooting war back to a cold war so far as the use of mass communication in the international sphere is concerned.

and we have the technical skill to operate it. The British Reuter's and our three great press associations serve more places than does Russia, outside the Russian orbit. The British and American radio are technically qualified and placed so as to blanket the globe. The American motion picture still retains leadership in mass ·popularity. Our resources, machinery, and skill in the making of books and magazines are as great as any.

The employment of American mass-communications resources for cold-war objectives, however, encounters a strong nonmaterial obstacle in our culture. Out of the liberal-democratic ideology and constitutional framework developed in the eighteenth century we have inherited the public policy that there shall be *no public policy*, no direction or supervision of mass communication. There is the faith that out of unregulated news most citizens winnow the facts, that putting the facts together makes an edifice called "truth," and that people's loyalties and emotions will attach themselves to this fact-fabricated truth. Thus the inherent American strength for international communication, from a technical point of view, may not be strength at all, so far as participation in a cold war is concerned.

The Russians, and some other peoples, on the other hand, start with *principles* to which they attach supreme loyalty and adherence; facts, for them, are selected to illustrate the principles. News, drama, and all mass communication are shaped to reinforce the principles. And so for them central governmental direction of the mass media is the only thing that makes sense. Propaganda and a cold war are things toward which they are attuned.[3]

MASS MEDIA AND PROMOTION OF A WORLD COMMUNITY

I have dwelt at length on the predominant uses to which the mass-communications machinery has hitherto been put in the international field—to promote nationalism, imperialism, and cold war and shooting war. This is not to say that any one or all of the modern media are especially adapted or fitted to these purposes rather than to

3. In the discussion of my paper at the Harris Institute on which this chapter was based, the point was made that at present the Iron Curtain prevents the United States from any considerable attempt to reach the people behind the curtain with what we hold to be the true picture of events, whereas Russia is free under our open system of communication to use the mass media —through speeches for the purpose at Lake Success and elsewhere—to reach the American people generally with their version of events. This might argue that as inventions the mass media favor the totalitarian type of government.

others. They are essentially neutral instruments whose influence is determined by those who control them.[4]

Let us suppose now that effective power were so disposed on our planet that a group of powerful nations or a single, independent instrument of authority should, as an objective, settle on the development in all peoples everywhere of a sympathetic understanding of the variety of customs, beliefs, religions, and ideologies of the nations that inhabit the earth and should emphasize the concepts of underlying human likeness which give man the basis for at least a minimum toleration of differences. There is no reason to think that the modern battery of mass media, with their variety, their reach, and their richness, would not be fully as effective instruments to help build a popular base for world government or community as hitherto they have been for nationalism, imperialism, and hatred. Especially with the advent of television, the mass media as a whole are today more powerful agents for divisiveness and destruction or for understanding and peace than they could have been a century ago.

The technical possibilities of integrated organization are seen as a kind of preview in the machinery already achieved for the postal and telephone systems. Both, it is true, are essentially means of private rather than of public communication. Both have been organized as national monopolies in each country and are connected with each other at the border by simple reciprocal agreements. What results was defined in the words of the 1875 International Postal Convention: "for the purpose of communication the whole of the signatory countries form one single territory"!

MASS COMMUNICATION AND THE IRON CURTAIN

There remain some miscellaneous speculations as to the social effects of the modern mass media. Have they made more difficult the successful maintenance of a Chinese wall or iron curtain which shuts

4. In the discussion of this point, an experienced news broadcaster expressed his doubt as to whether the new medium of radio, at least, possessed the quality of neutrality as between its use for socially constructive and for social disintegrating purposes. The reason suggested was that the wider audience appeal of negative, sharp criticism and sensationalism created a program tendency in that direction. Another member of the group thought that because of the frequency of appearance of newspapers and radio broadcasts, and their active competition with each other for attention, they tend almost inevitably to magnify the significance of small changes, to underline and to glamorize small events out of all proportion, so that people get an unreal and distorted picture of what actually happens. These are certainly characteristics of the mass media—emphasizing combat, sensation, and glamorization. But I do not believe they destroy the concept of the instruments as available for promoting quite contrary objectives and in that sense neutral as technical instruments.

out all communication from outside a nation's borders or prevents access from the outside to knowledge of what happens inside its borders?

Our review of the list of inventions indicates that most of them require the co-operation of public agencies within a country in order that material communicated from the outside may enter. This is true of all but the radio broadcast and possibly also of leaflets dropped from an airplane. (Even mail and telephone messages can be intercepted at the border.) Experience with countries such as Germany, Italy, and Japan during the recent war indicates that policing of radio sets and jamming of broadcasts greatly reduced, but did not completely cut off, clandestine listening. How effective the Iron Curtain was and is in Russia I do not know. It is safe to say, however, that if there is a dissident group in Russia or in any other sizable country, it can, through international radio, get the news of the outside world.

If a country stops short of erecting an iron curtain, maintains some of the usual forms of external intercourse, but practices regulation and censorship, the battery of modern mass media reduces appreciably the possibilities of completely uncorrected distortions and national isolationism. Thus it can be said that modern techniques of mass communication work definitely but not decisively against the effectiveness of the Chinese wall or iron curtain. They certainly make insulation more difficult.

MASS COMMUNICATION AND CULTURAL IMPERIALISM

Quite aside from consciously directed propaganda aimed at a specific territory by an aggressive power, is there an unconscious cultural "imperialism" affecting smaller neighboring territory involved in the operation of the mass media by a large, powerful, and culturally vital state?

It is hard to isolate the influence of the mass media from the complex of other factors which tend toward the cultural absorption of, or influence on, smaller by larger states. But especially where there is language identity between the neighboring states, cultural extension seems to be a contributing social effect of the newer mass media, especially of cheap books, mass magazines (more particularly of picture and comic magazines), motion pictures, and radio. The phenomenon can be observed in Bermuda and Canada vis-à-vis the United States,

Belgium vis-à-vis France, and Norway (where English is a second language) vis-à-vis Great Britain.

MASS COMMUNICATION AND LARGE-SCALE ORGANIZATION

Do the newer mass media themselves not only tend to become large-scale organizations but also to facilitate the effective operation of large-scale industrial, social, and political activities with widely scattered agencies and offices? The evidence seems to be clearly in the affirmative. By the full use of a teletyping network, facsimile transmission, and the telephone, supplemented by cheap, rapid printing, and the instructional cinema, a central office can keep in hour-by-hour, two-way contact with field offices scattered over a continental area or even over the globe. Again, mass communication does not create big business, big government, or the Great Society. But it greatly facilitates their administration.

MASS COMMUNICATION AND DIPLOMACY

Do the newer mass media, with their persistent prying for news-pictures-comments, have an effect on diplomatic negotiations which changes their character? Yes. Since 1900 and before, the press has entered as a factor in diplomatic negotiations; incidents have been manipulated by diplomats to build backfires and to launch trial balloons. And, more recently, conferences have been used as the base for propaganda campaigns through publicized conference speeches.

But negotiation is *still* negotiation. As photographers and reporters invade a committee, the negotiators move their necessary tentative and exploratory activities to a subcommittee, to a private luncheon table, or to an upper hotel room. Even under the most modern klieg lights a Churchill and Roosevelt "arrange things" by private telephone, personal letter, and face-to-face talk.

What is changed in diplomatic negotiations since the Congress of Vienna is that now the state negotiations about important matters involve widespread discussions, the marshaling of general opinion, and a dramatic public debate as well as private preliminary negotiation.[5]

5. There were several additional speculations by members of the group, during the discussion, regarding the social effect of rapid transport by plane, the telephone, and teletype, on diplomatic intercourse.

One member suggested that modern political leaders are increasingly persons who succeed by speaking to large, indiscriminate audiences; that they tend to be taken in by the propaganda they repeat (see Hitler's and Mussolini's state papers). The effect of such propaganda-

MASS COMMUNICATION AND THE BABEL OF TONGUES

Finally, do the mass-communications media affect the language barriers which stand athwart easy international intercourse? In an important sense, no. The mass media must accommodate themselves to the language pluralities of the world—through translation of texts, beaming broadcasts in different languages to different groups, dubbing in movie dialogue, etc. But, in another sense, the media tend to reduce language diversity. In so far as they deal in pictures, charts, and animated cartoon, they are talking an international language. And in so far as radio programs, magazines, and books are produced with technical skill and distributed widely from countries of large size and wealth, the language they employ becomes increasingly a second language to many people elsewhere. Such natural extensions of familiarity with the languages of major use (English, French, Russian, Chinese) argue for the gradual adoption of one or another as a predominant regional or international language rather than any artificially constructed language.

SUMMARY

The main social influence to be reckoned with in the case of modern inventions in the field of mass communication is that together they are becoming a greater influence on popular attitude, loyalty, understanding, and prejudice in comparison with the older, intimate, quiet influences of face-to-face groups.[6] The mass media are not another

---

success leaders might be thought of as a deterioration in quality of policy formation, both domestic and foreign.

Another point made in discussion was that the new media throw much more control of foreign policy into the hands of the persons at the top in the center and reduce the flexibility and skill in negotiation of the diplomats in the field. Contrariwise, a group member who had served in a diplomatic post felt that the newer media enabled people in the field to bring their own observations and field experience to bear more quickly, fully, and flexibly on the home office—in other words, that the telephone is a two-way affair.

Still another person with diplomatic experience felt that the press invasion of conferences, with an insistence on the open arrival at open covenants, greatly hampered the act of negotiation. With the necessity of stating a position at the outset, any change made later in order to arrive at agreement becomes a defeat.

6. The point was made in discussion that people are still much more influenced in attitude by a personal conversation than by reading a dozen general newspapers and that we are much more influenced by special journals of small circulation than by the great general mass media: i.e., trade-union people by labor papers, professors by professional journals, businessmen by newsletters.

I do not, however, claim any absolute or decisive change from face-to-face influence to mass-media influence. My argument was on a more-or-less basis, and the claim is that mass media have more influence now than was true a century ago, especially the media such as motion pictures and television which can communicate so fully and richly. I would also ematom bomb. They represent a gradual rather than a sudden impact of invention on institutions. But, like the bomb, they may truly be regarded as a social weapon that can do much to build a peaceful, happy world or to accelerate a process of confusion and disintegration.

─────────

phasize, as did other members of the group, that a co-ordinated, orchestrated use of all the media over a considerable period for a single set of purposes may have a greater impact than we now imagine, on the basis of our experience with the diverse purposes and discontinuous programs of the media in the United States. There was some testimony from persons who had observed the use of the media during wars where there was general unity of purpose, and during the Hitler regime in Germany, that together the media are a formidable influence.

But I am fully in accord with the notion that face-to-face experiences are the major determinants of opinion, attitude, and prejudice. A valuable comment in the discussion was that army experience indicated that the motion picture is the most efficient mass media for changing attitudes and that it is only efficient where persons have not previously formed judgments or fixed attitudes.

NEW TECHNIQUES OF WAR AND NATIONAL POLICIES

By Bernard Brodie

IN CONTRAST to the titles of five other papers in this series, which contain such phrases as "international relations" or "world order," the assignment given this writer refers to the effect of new techniques of war on "national policies." It is therefore appropriate to interpret "national policies" in this context to refer to security policy whether the subjects of that policy be foreign or domestic. For the modern world it is perhaps in any case as logical to distinguish between security and welfare policies, both of which have foreign and domestic implications, as to adhere to the traditional though equally arbitrary distinction between foreign policy and domestic policy.

PRELIMINARY CONSIDERATIONS

It is important to notice at the outset that we are dealing here with two distinct but related problems. The first concerns the effects of changes in technology and in other human capacities on the techniques of waging war. One must include the "other human capacities" because, after all, total mobilization requires devices of an economic and political nature which were wholly unthought of prior to 1914 and which represent social inventions quite as ingenious and as far-reaching in their consequences as the changes in military technology. The second problem is to determine the effects of the new military techniques thus evolved upon national policies.

Speculation on the first problem demands conversance with basic strategic principles and some familiarity with things scientific and technological. The latter problem, on the other hand, demands *in addition* consideration of psychological, social, economic, and political factors upon which—in this particular context—the available data are all too sparse and nebulous. Also, the errors resulting from the former speculation become, equally with the valid judgments, the premises of the latter, and in the process they are subject to a certain multiplier action. The least, therefore, we should ask of ourselves is some measure of humility concerning our conclusions. The number and magnitude of the variables are almost overwhelming.

As a matter of fact, the limited historical data we do have indicate that national policies have been about as often based upon erroneous judgments of the military significance of current technological trends as upon correct judgments. The error may be due to underestimation of the degree or rate of technological progress to be expected of a new development or to overestimation.[1] It may be due to a misapprehension of the strategic effect of a given technological trend even when that trend itself is more or less correctly forecast.[2] It has happened in the past that a very serious error of policy resulted from a wrong identification of the potential enemy.[3] Also, in some contexts relatively minor developments will help to stimulate or provoke panic;[4]

1. The overestimation has usually, but not aways, been relative, involving an underestimation of the progress to be expected of various countering weapons. Thus, the introduction of the shell gun in naval warfare in the 1830's prompted predictions that the large warship (and with it British naval supremacy) was a thing of the past. The subsequent introduction of iron armor stimulated the contrary conviction—that it was feasible to construct an "impregnable" ship. Jellicoe's handling of the British Grand Fleet at Jutland was largely governed by his fear of German torpedoes, which in fact did so little damage as to argue that the British admiral exaggerated in his mind the potentialities of the weapon as of that time. The greatly exaggerated expectations inherent in the "air supremacy" theories of General Douhet and Brigadier General "Billy" Mitchell resulted partly from an underestimation of the development to be expected of certain counterair weapons, such as antiaircraft guns, and partly from a gross overestimation of the amount of physical damage which could reasonably be expected on land and sea targets from a given weight of chemical bombs (the only kind they could consider). Another overestimation which had tremendous strategic consequences was that which the British navy and government placed upon the effectiveness of the "Asdic" (supersonic detecting device against submarines) prior to World War II.

2. Perhaps the most conspicuous historical example is the confusion which attended the introduction of the steam warship, which on both sides of the Channel was interpreted by many as favoring France at the expense of Great Britain (see my *Sea Power in the Machine Age* [2d ed.; Princeton, 1943], chap. iv).

3. Thus, the French in the late nineteenth and early twentieth centuries vigorously promoted the development of the submarine as the weapon which would destroy British naval supremacy, only to face the threat of ruin from that instrument when Great Britain became the chief ally of France against Germany.

4. The introduction of the British battleship "Dreadnought" (1906), which had an important influence on the current British-German naval race, illustrates this principle in two ways. In the first place, when measured against the innovations of the fifteen years preceding and of the eight or ten years following, it did not represent nearly so novel a departure either in design or in fighting effectiveness as contemporaries and also later historians generally assumed. Second, it was overlooked in that instance, as it has been in many others, that it usually requires numbers to make a new design of combat instrument strategically important. As one British former Admiralty official expressed it in reference to the much more radical innovation of the introduction of the ironclad: "It is deplorable that out of this expectation of novelty and progress in every newly designed vessel has grown a tendency to regard as comparatively useless all vessels of earlier date and less formidable power." If this were acceptable, he continued, "the greatest Naval Power henceforward would not be that which possessed the greatest aggregate of force, but that which possessed the most powerful ship" (Sir William White, "Our Unarmoured Ships," *Colburn's United Service Magazine*, September, 1873).

in others the most revolutionary changes will fail to disturb complacency among public and politicians. Nor can it be assumed that the context which promotes complacency is necessarily one in which friendly and pacific relations prevail with other states. Certainly the complacency which ruled in Great Britain in the mid-1930's had other bases.

The formulation of security policy is, after all, a matter of anticipation of probabilities—as qualified by considerations of what is politically possible, feasible, or safe—on the part of persons who, whether responsible by nature or not, at least have enormous responsibility thrust upon them. As politicians these persons have neither the time nor the inclination to preoccupy themselves, as some scholars or strategists may do, with the long-term significance of changes in military technology, and rarely the competence to make anything of it if they do. The Churchills, who are temperamentally disposed toward toying with strategic and tactical concepts, are rare sports among their breed. Most political leaders must rely upon the advice of their military aides, who belong to a profession long recognized as markedly conservative (though it is possible to exaggerate the character and magnitude of that conservatism), who have vested service and personal interests which influence them consciously or unconsciously, whose talents are not primarily dialectic, and who are likewise saddled with tremendous responsibility. Responsibility usually demands that one hedge one's bets, for pretty much the same reason that life insurance companies are required by law to follow a conservative investment policy. We are therefore not likely to find military leaders, or the politicians whom they advise, accepting completely, upon the advent of some revolutionary military device, that drastic adjustment which free and objective inquiry may indicate as necessary or at least desirable.

Moreover, we must concede in passing that the conservative military outlook (reflected, for example, in excessive resort to the axiom of Jomini that "methods change but principles are unchanging") has had in the past a good many opportunities of saying "I told you so." The anchor to windward, while it has often proved costly through excessive drag, has also—with sufficient frequency to be impressive— served to avoid disaster. For example, even if one concludes that the battleship is today an obsolete instrument (and whether one does so or not must depend in part on just what one means by "obsolete"), one must nevertheless acknowledge that the battleship type has been charged with being obsolete on and off for well over one hundred years. The estimate which was proved true only after so long a delay must be deemed to have been wrong for most of the time that it was entertained.

Similarly, if one had to take part in a debate on whether Billy Mitchell or General Douhet was an accurate prophet of World War II, one could probably make as strong case for the negative in each case as for the affirmative. The question is not affected by whether or not either or both may be proved right in a third world war. The stock market usually deals severely with those speculators whose predictions are correct in character and degree but not in timing. The issues of war and of national policy are not less rigorous in their penalties for errors of timing. For the purpose of policy decisions, a short-term forecast which is correct in timing is likely to be a good deal more useful than a long-term forecast which indicates only trends.

The fact is that what looks on the surface like simple conservatism may often be due to a wider comprehension of all the factors operating in a situation than is enjoyed by the person of more visionary outlook. This is not to suggest that such is the *usual* explanation of conservatism in military matters. One must avoid giving undue credit even to those correct intuitions which are held so rigidly and uncritically as to be practically indistinguishable from prejudices. The person who is one time right for the wrong reasons may also on an equally important occasion be disastrously wrong for the very same reasons. But there are several good reasons why the person who is not swept off his feet by the advent of some new device frequently turns out at the critical moment to have been right after all.

First, it is too often overlooked that technology marches on with a broad sweep, that the development which commands attention may be in process of having its effectiveness diminished or even nullified by some concurrent development which is either too unobtrusive or unspectacular to draw attention or is being carried on in secret. One must not push that point too far. One should be especially dubious of the degree of its applicability to an innovation of such radical and far-reaching consequences as the atomic bomb. Besides, except in relative terms which permit of wide latitudes of effectiveness, it is simply not true historically (to quote a distinguished American admiral) that "there has never yet been a weapon against which man has been unable to devise a counter-weapon or defense." Nevertheless, the examples even in recent history when the point has been valid and significant are much too numerous to catalogue.

Second, we must remember that technology is not all that matters. In the summer of 1940 it seemed that Great Britain could not possibly stand against the odds that faced her and that conclusive defeat before the end of the year was practically a certainty. Was it bull-headedness, chauvinism, or a deeper insight which induced British leaders to reject that view? Somewhere deep in the national heritage was a trait which had survived more than a century of industrial revolution and a generation of political and social disillusionment and which was to save Britain and British liberties once again. We are speaking here of the morale factor, which Napoleon considered to have thrice the importance of the material, which may be more rather than less important in an age of atomic bombs, and which is not the only factor operating to qualify the significance of the technological factor in war.

A third point is one which would hardly have been worth considering prior to Hiroshima but which may in the future be of increasing importance. As the atomic bomb and other weapons tend under some circumstances to raise what Professor Harold Lasswell has called the "critical level of exacerbation" in international affairs, there develops the possibility that a nation which may be incapable of fighting a total war may still exercise many if not all the prerogatives and responsibilities of a great power in crises short of total war. For example, if it were concluded that the United Kingdom is hopelessly vulnerable to new forms of attack from the Continent, that conclusion might nevertheless have to be discounted even in calculations of British military-political capabilities. In a world which, however beset by antagonisms, is universally loath to pull the trigger starting a third world war, the ability to project substantial power abroad in "troubled areas" might have a significance quite separate from the issue of vulnerability at home. That is especially likely to be true if Great Britain is allied, formally or informally, to a nation like our own which is not comparably vulnerable.

We may now turn to a consideration of certain specific technological developments which appear bound to have such obvious and far-reaching effects upon techniques of waging war as to oblige political and military leaders to make substantial adjustment in their security policies. In doing so, it is impossible to avoid concentrating attention mainly upon the atomic bomb. Those other new military techniques which are presently in process of development are likely to prove significant mainly in the extent to which they enhance and supplement the effectiveness of the atomic bomb or diminish it. For example, the very-long-range rocket (V-2 type) is important primarily in that it may ultimately become the vehicle of an atomic attack, though at present that possibility seems relatively remote. On the other hand, ground-to-air rockets and air-to-air rockets (for use against enemy aircraft) may prove most important in the degree to which they qualify the effectiveness of atomic attack. Even bacteriological warfare is likely to develop, if at all, as an adjunct to atomic war rather than as something to be used quite independently of the latter.

THE ATOMIC BOMB COMPARED WITH PREVIOUS WEAPONS

The impact of the atomic bomb on United States policy has thus far been evidenced most clearly in the almost frantic effort to secure the adoption of a system of international control of atomic energy. It is difficult if not impossible to find a historical precedent for the eagerness with which this nation has pursued an endeavor which, if successful, would deprive it of the advantages of monopoly possession of a decisive military weapon. To be sure, the monopoly is bound to be temporary, but that has always been true of new weapons, the monopoly possession of which has usually been jealously guarded for as long as possible. Indeed, the United States is even now behaving in the customary manner concerning all new weapons other than those based on the explosive release of atomic energy, a fact which in itself sufficiently demonstrates that the exceptional American position on atomic-energy control is based on something other than national generosity. That "something other" is of course a well-warranted fear of living in a world which morally and politically is little different from the one we have known but which in addition is characterized by multilateral possession of atomic armaments.

However, while the fear persists, the trend in the United States has apparently been away from panic rather than toward it. The habit of living with the bomb would itself sufficiently account for that trend, though there have also been other factors at work which will shortly be reviewed. What the situation will be when the United States acquires the knowledge or the firm suspicion that the Soviet Union too is producing atomic bombs is another matter, consideration of which we can also postpone for the moment. At any rate, our government has apparently hardened in its resolve that any international control scheme must contain within itself practically watertight guaranties against violation and evasion. And, in so far as data are available, there is every indication that this resolve enjoys overwhelming public support.

Perhaps the most important as well as immediate consequence of this attitude is that it greatly lessens the possibility that an international control system will in fact be achieved. Indeed, American leadership in securing formal suspension of the activities of the United Nations Atomic Energy Commission is open acknowledgment of that fact. Thus, we must look forward to a period of national adjustment to the prospect of living in an atomic age devoid of effective international controls. That does not mean that efforts to secure such controls will necessarily languish. But it does mean that other forms of adjustment will receive a good deal more public attention and support than they have thus far. It will mean particularly a heightened emphasis on anticipating the character of a war fought with atomic bombs, with a view both to taking all reasonable precautions against the terrible hazards of such a conflict and to securing victory if it must come. The latter goal may appear a mockery to many sensitive minds, but it is not likely to appear such to those responsible for national policy, especially since the argument that visible strength is the best guaranty against war is not easily refuted to the public satisfaction.

We must therefore attempt to predict, first, the effects of the atomic bomb upon the military services of the future and, second, the character and extent of civilian adjustment to military needs. Among the many variables which bear upon our predictions, the most important by far is summed up by the following question: "How many bombs can one expect to find in existence any given number of years hence, and how will they be distributed among the nations?" All our conclusions depend upon the answer to that question, yet it is curious how consistently this issue has been slighted or ignored in the general debate on the destiny of the armed forces. Each view expressed usually reflects a certain presumption concerning numbers and distribution of atomic bombs, but the specific presumption being applied is rarely isolated and acknowledged. It may be said in general that those who stress the completely revolutionary character of the bomb are tacitly presuming that in the not-too-distant future it will become relatively abundant, while the conservatives tend to presume that it will remain inordinately scarce. Neither side, however, shows much evidence of being aware of the specific presumption it has made, let alone of having weighed the validity of that presumption.

In fact, with our present lack of knowledge it is difficult to say what range of numbers must be regarded as representing abundance. For example, in the paper prepared by the War Department in March, 1947, on "The Effects of the Atomic Bomb on National Security," there is a reference to something called a "significant" number of bombs. The meaning of "significant" is then explained only as indicating that number of bombs which would "provide an important military capability."[5] The Army may have specific numbers in mind when it uses such terms, but the chances are that it does not. We know that one bomb will not win a war against a major power (it took two to produce the surrender of an already defeated Japan), and the same may reasonably be held to be true of five or ten. But we have little idea what number is "significant," and even less conception of how many it takes to make the weapon "decisive." Much will, of course, depend on how the bombs are used, but then the number available will in large part govern the way in which they are employed.

We do, to be sure, have a good deal of experience with strategic bombing from the recent war, and it would appear superficially that, by merely computing the number of atomic bombs it would take (using the evidence of Hiroshima and Nagasaki) to wreak the destruction done with TNT bombs and incendiaries, we would have some measure of the number of atomic bombs necessary to achieve "significant" or "decisive" results. We have been told, for example, by excellent authority that with each plane loaded with ten tons of TNT bombs and incendiaries it would have required some 210 B-29's at Hiroshima and 120 B-29's at Nagasaki to accomplish the damage done at each of those places with one plane carrying an atomic bomb. The same source suggests that, if the more powerful Nagasaki bomb had been used at Hiroshima, the damage done to the latter city could have been equaled only by 270 B-29's loaded with ten tons each of nonatomic explosives.[6]

These figures are no doubt very useful in suggesting a means of

5. The War Department paper is included in Bernard Brodie and Eilene Galloway, *The Atomic Bomb and the Armed Services* ("Public Affairs Bulletin," No. 55 [Washington, D.C.: Legislative Reference Service, Library of Congress, May, 1947]). The specific reference cited above is on p. 67 of the bulletin.

6. The United States Strategic Bombing Survey, *The Effects of Atomic Bombs on Hiroshima and Nagasaki* (Washington, D.C.: Government Printing Office, 1946), p. 33.

arriving at the factor of increase of power of the atomic bomb over the TNT bomb—a far better means unquestionably than that of merely computing the relative amounts of energy released. But the difficulty is that the two types of bombs are not really comparable in strictly quantitative terms. In some respects the atomic bomb is more destructive than the comparison given above would indicate; in other respects it is less so. Let us see why. First, it is clear that, while heat and blast effects are common to both atomic and nonatomic bombs, the element of radioactivity in the former introduces a new factor which is profoundly significant both for human casualties and for the enduring contamination of bombed areas. Second, the fact that a given amount of damage can be effected in a far shorter period of time with atomic bombs than with conventional bombs has enormous implications in terms of the ability of the target state to repair damage and to adjust its defenses to the attack. For example, by the middle of 1944 Germany was still going strong, and it could hardly be said that the strategic bombing to which she had been subject during the previous five years had yet accomplished anything like "decisive" results. For one thing, it had not been strictly cumulative. But if the same amount of destruction—or even half the amount—had been telescoped into, say, one week, it is hard to imagine how that nation could have been anything other than completely prostrate. Third, the effective bombing range with an atomic bomb of a plane like the B-29 is, for reasons which will be mentioned later in this chapter, potentially much greater than that of the same plane carrying ordinary explosives. Fourth, there is the matter of psychological impact, the terror effects of the atomic bomb, the proportions of which we can scarcely begin to predict. True, in the recent war the human animal showed himself capable of adjusting to heavy bombing raids to an astonishing degree, but at least he was given the opportunity to get adjusted through the very gradualness with which the bombing attack reached its crescendo. Moreover, the knowledge that some two or three thousand aircraft were approaching a certain city was an unmistakable signal to the inhabitants of that city to repair to air-raid shelters, and at least in part an "all-clear" signal to the inhabitants of other cities far removed—both of which characteristics are likely to be absent in a situation where individual planes carry the means of destroying whole sections of large cities.

On the other hand, there are at least two factors, apart from the issue of possible scarcity, which suggest the necessity of discounting somewhat the "factor of increase of power" which might otherwise be attributed to the atomic bomb over the TNT bomb. First, there is the tactical question. A single plane may, as at Hiroshima, accomplish an amount of destruction comparable to that effected by 210 similar planes carrying ordinary bombs—provided it arrives over the target. But if the area is strongly defended, a force of 210 aircraft might be able to get the great majority of its planes through where a single plane would have no chance whatever. If planes bearing atomic bombs have to be attended by large numbers of decoys (perhaps armed with ordinary bombs) and fighters, the advantage of economy in logistics and operations otherwise accruing to the atomic bomb is largely lost. However, it is also true that under some conditions a single plane has a better chance of reaching its target than a large force. Second, since the atomic bomb in its minimum efficient size is necessarily of "city-buster" destructiveness, there are relatively few targets on which its full destructive power can be utilized. Even Nagasaki, because of its configuration, suffered much less damage than Hiroshima, despite the fact that the Nagasaki bomb was more powerful. When we say that a plane carrying an atomic bomb can do the same amount of damage as two hundred or three hundred planes carrying conventional bombs, we are speaking of an exceptionally favorable target. We must therefore consider the effectiveness of a bomb partly at least in terms of the target. It happens, of course, that the most appropriate of indicated targets—that is, the large city—is an extraordinarily important one. It may be used on other targets if it is plentiful enough, but on most other targets its relative advantage over TNT bombs will not be nearly so great. On the other hand, we must ask ourselves whether it would ever have to be used on "other targets" after the main cities of a nation were destroyed.

These are only the more outstanding of the considerations which affect the question of how many bombs are "significant" and how many could be considered a "decisive" force. It can readily be seen that the magnitude of the terror created might well make a rather small number decisive, and then again it might not, depending largely on the preparation of the target population, psychological and otherwise, and on their degree of awareness or ignorance of what is going on (in this case ignorance might be an asset). In any case, there is a large problem area here demanding a great deal of intensive investigation. The essential question to be answered is: "How many bombs will do what?" And the "what" must be reckoned in over-all strategic results rather than merely in acres destroyed.

However, if our present knowledge is closely confined, our ignorance also has its limits. For the best of political reasons we are not being told the current rate of United States production of atomic bombs, but even the most conservative guess would lead us to conclude that the number which will have accumulated after, say, ten years of production will certainly be "significant." And we know also that for purposes of planning ten years is not a long time. It is less than half the normal life-expectancy of a cruiser. Thus, there is no time like the present to begin to think of how wars will be fought when the atomic bombs available to one or both belligerents will be numbered at least in scores and possibly in hundreds.

THE FOUR CONDITIONS OF ATOMIC-WAR STRATEGY

As we project into the future the effects of the atomic bomb upon the armed services, we must distinguish between at least four different phases or conditions: (1) American monopoly expressed in a small number of bombs; (2) American monopoly with a relatively large number of bombs; (3) the end of American monopoly but with the United States still enjoying a large margin of superiority over its major rival both in atomic bombs and in the means of delivering them; and (4) the end not only of monopoly but of significant American superiority.

Here again we are using terms like "small" and "relatively large" without any effort at precision, but for the reasons already given we are obliged to do so and will continue to be obliged to do so until we have more knowledge than yet possessed by any one person. Nevertheless, these rough distinctions have value in organizing our thoughts. They indicate, at the very minimum, that to distinguish merely between the monopoly period and the post-monopoly period —as is usually done—is not enough. Thus, the position described under (3) above, while probably not so favorable as that described under (2), is nevertheless not an adverse one, and it may last much longer. It may even be a more favorable position than that described under (1). And it is apparent that each situation requires a distinctive strategy.

The situation described under (1), "American monopoly with a small number of bombs," is certainly that situation in which we found ourselves immediately following the end of the war. It may be the situation we are in at this writing, depending on (*a*) our current rate of production and (*b*) the old question of how many bombs is a "small" number.

Although we must know the answers to these questions to determine just how long this situation will last, if it is still with us, we do know that it is bound to be very limited in time. For example, even if our present rate of production of atomic bombs should be as low as two a month (a wholly random figure), the continuation of that rate would result in ten years' time in the accumulation of the materials for some 240 atomic bombs, which could hardly be called a "small" number.

Situation (2), "American monopoly with a relatively large number of bombs," would, of course, not occur at all if our monopoly should be broken by a rival state in the very near future. But if the more optimistic predictions (from our point of view) concerning Russian capabilities to produce the bomb are true, this situation might last from five to ten years, possibly longer. The military strategy dictated by this situation is distinctly and perhaps drastically different from that indicated under situation (1).

The situation mentioned under (3) above suggests that the end of monopoly need not and probably will not spell the immediate end of decisive superiority, especially when we remember that what counts is not the atomic bomb alone but also the vehicles and devices connected with its use. It is too generally forgotten that our position vis-à-vis the Soviet Union in atomic warfare will be much better on the day the Russians produce their first bomb than it is at present, for the simple reason that we will then have many more bombs, perhaps several times as many, as we do now. It may be true that our *monopoly* is a "wasting asset," since it is bound soon or later to run out, and we are always getting closer to the day it does so. But our *superiority* will increase considerably before it begins to wane; it may continue to increase even after the Soviet Union is producing bombs; and it may be a long time in waning thereafter. If the raw materials available in the world for the production of atomic bombs are as limited as some seem to think, this situation may be a permanent one, that is, it may not in our time give way to situation (4).

Situation (4), "the end not only of monopoly but also of significant American superiority," envisages the two-way war with atomic bombs which is most discussed even though most remote in time. How remote in time it is must remain for the time being a huge question mark. Certainly we must include it in our thinking as a possibility to be reckoned with even within the next ten years. But within such a time period it is hardly the most likely contingency and, at any rate, is not the one for which our policy-makers will plan exclusively.

It is, of course, very difficult to define in simple terms what superiority or the lack of it must involve. For example, a three-to-one margin of superiority might be very significant if the total number of bombs in existence was reckoned in scores or even hundreds, but would be much less significant if the number was reckoned in thousands, since in the latter case the side with the smaller number might nevertheless have enough to win decisive results in a surprise attack. Similarly, as already indicated, the side which has the best means of delivering the bomb has an advantage which may either implement a superiority in numbers of bombs or offset an inferiority in numbers. And the "means of delivery" definitely must include "sabotage" devices as well as aircraft or rockets, though one must not regard as easy the laying of bombs by secret means.

We may now take up these situations one by one and attempt to see what each of them means for the strategy of war. We must confine ourselves to broad outlines, because we are likely enough to be in error even if we do so, and we are bound to be in error if we attempt to construct the details as well. We must also isolate out the possibility of revolutionary developments comparable to the atomic bomb, such as might occur in bacteriology, though we must, of course, reckon with pronounced evolutionary advances in the weapons we now know.

AMERICAN WAR STRATEGY UNDER CONDITIONS OF MONOPOLY

Situation (1): American monopoly expressed in a small number of bombs.—The strategy of this situation must obviously conform closely to the strategy followed before the advent of the atomic bomb. In other words, the role and general composition of each of the existing services remains pretty much unchanged. The two questions of chief importance are (*a*) how the relatively few atomic bombs available should be used if war should occur during this period and (*b*) to what extent and in what way the services should begin to remodel themselves in anticipation of succeeding phases.

This is the period during which we may accept as presumably valid the dictum of General H. H. Arnold that "the great unit cost of the atomic bomb means that as nearly as possible every one must be delivered to its intended target."[7] To make the statement strictly correct, one must substitute the word "scarcity" for the words "unit cost." Once the shooting begins, the unit cost paid at some date in the past is of no consequence whatever, but the existing scarcity, which may have been in part dictated by that cost, does make it necessary to seek maximum effectiveness of each of the bombs in hand.

General Arnold, in amplifying the statement quoted above, goes on to state that the very heavy bomber (i.e., B-29 or larger) is as yet the only way to deliver the atomic bomb, and he adds that delivery with such a vehicle can be "certain of success only when the user has air superiority." Since air superiority presumably depends largely upon vigorous fighter-plane support of attacking bombers, and since fighters are inevitably of much lesser range than large bombers, the implication is that bombers operating from distant bases are not *by themselves* a sufficiently reliable means of delivering atomic bombs. They or at least their supporting fighters must have bases close enough to the enemy so that the latter can operate over the targets. To be sure, one must consider the likelihood of the independent use of very high-speed jet-propelled bombers, but these types, too, are for the present of substantially shorter range than conventional propeller-driven aircraft of like size.

Thus, a probable basic requirement for the effective use of atomic bombs under the conditions here envisaged would be the acquisition and development of air bases relatively close to the enemy targets. With types of aircraft now in service that would mean at least as close as Iwo Jima is to Japan. Presumably, too, the scarcity of the bombs would militate against their all being expended in one brief bombing campaign. Thus, the advanced bases would, if held from the outset, have to be made secure. And, if not so held, they would have to be won and developed. In each case not only time is required but also the services of large sea, land, and air forces, roughly comparable in character to those of the last war. To be sure, if it proves feasible to launch atomic-bomb-carrying planes from aircraft carriers, the initial use of atomic bombs could come quite early in the war even if we did not already possess bases close to the enemy.

The conventional land, sea, and air forces would have to be brought into play not only to acquire the means of effectively launching atomic bombs, but—since we are postulating a relatively small num-

7. See his *Third Report to the Secretary of War, November 12, 1946*, p. 68 (printed ed.).

ber of bombs—to win the war. By definition, bombs which are "scarce" are insufficient in number to be decisive. One can therefore not expect that the major lines of strategy will be drawn with the use of atomic bombs primarily in mind. The atomic bomb will instead be considered a weapon of opportunity, to be used when circumstances indicate its use, and not something which dictates primary preoccupation with creating suitable circumstances.

It should incidentally be observed that if the atomic bomb is used as an ancillary weapon rather than a primary one, one of the chief military advantages ordinarily attributed to it is lost. From the point of view of logistics and of mobilization of war potential, the important thing about the atomic bomb is not that one bomb can destroy a city but that *one plane* can destroy a city. But if it is so scarce that it can be used "only when the user has air superiority," that is, only when the situation has been well prepared in advance and when the plane carrying the atomic bomb is attended on its mission by a large number of other planes, then one must conclude that it will make strategic bombing more effective without essentially changing the gigantic character of the effort from that which had to go into the strategic bombing campaigns of World War II.

Whether or not the strategy here described would really be applicable to a war fought in the near future, the fact is that our military leaders appear to be accepting it as applicable. If that be so, it is possible that they are underestimating the strategic effects to be gained from a bolder use of even a small number of atomic bombs. The stipulation that so far as possible each one must be delivered to its intended target has implications which conceivably might diminish rather than enhance the military effectiveness of the bombs available.

Situation (2): American monopoly with a large number of bombs.— To avoid reviving the question—which remains to be answered satisfactorily—of what is a "large" number of bombs, let us assume arbitrarily that by "large number" we mean one measured in three figures. Thus, if our present rate of production were two bombs per month and were to continue unchanged, our accumulation of atomic bombs (or rather the materials for assembling them) would be entering the "large numbers" category about four or five years hence.

There are at least two criteria separating this situation from the one described previously in terms of the method of using the bomb. First, the atomic bomb is now the primary weapon of strategic bombing, which is itself the decisive instrument of attack. Second, the possession of a large number of bombs indicates the acceptance of substantial wastage in their use. As is true of every missile fired in war, it is still *desirable* that every bomb reach its intended target. But since, as we have seen, the rigid stipulation that it do so is bound severely to limit and circumscribe its use, insistence upon it must frustrate full realization of the gigantic offensive potentialities of this new weapon.

All that is suggested here is the application to the atomic bomb of principles which govern the use of all other implements of warfare. The atomic bomb provides, potentially at least, the cheapest way of destroying enemy cities, but, paradoxically, that cheapness can be realized only if the user pushes out of his mind consideration of unit cost of the individual bomb. Only if he does so can he conceive of those bold uses of the bomb which will result in the maximum damage to the enemy in the briefest possible time.

Since we are assuming a situation in which we feel fairly confident the enemy has no atomic bombs, there is little reason why we should hesitate to expend the bulk of the bombs early in the war, before enemy defenses are alerted or at least before they reach their optimum organization. The surprise and shock value of a devastating raid early in the hostilities is bound to be far greater than one of equal magnitude later on. What do these postulates suggest for the strategy of attack?

In the first place, so long as we had long-range bombers capable of delivering the bombs from bases already in our possession, it would be foolish and wasteful to withhold our bombs until we had reached bases closer to the enemy. Closer bases would no doubt enable us to give strong fighter support to our invading bombers and would thus provide both greater security for those bombers and a great percentage of hits with our bombs. But offsetting those advantages would be the time and cost spent in acquiring and developing the advanced bases and the adjustments which that time would permit the enemy. Or perhaps some compromise scheme would be preferable, such as that of using perhaps half the bombs in an initial long-range blow to disorganize the enemy and then using the important advantage gained to seize the advanced bases (which should now be much easier to accomplish) for the more methodical use of the remaining bombs. But what seems on the face of it *not* to be indicated is a concern from first to last with getting every atomic bomb on its intended target.

Now is it feasible to launch an atomic-bomb attack upon a distant great power such as the Soviet Union from bases already in our possession or likely to be available to us within a very few years? On the basis of technical performance even of types of aircraft now in service the answer would seem to be "Yes," and it should certainly be in the affirmative with new types of aircraft already existing in experimental models.

It must always be remembered that, from the point of view of military economics, a plane which has delivered an atomic bomb has paid for itself many times over, and upon making the sortie the plane must therefore be regarded as being at least as expendable as is the bomb itself. This freedom from the necessity of retrieving the aircraft means in effect a one-way flight, and therefore an approximate doubling of what is usually regarded as the "effective bombing range" of the plane. The crew (if there be one) is another matter. Strictly from the point of view of military bookkeeping, it too could be regarded as expendable. Other considerations will, however, influence the enterprise and perhaps prevail; but in any case it is not necessary that the crew members return to their jumping-off point in the same plane in which they departed. All sorts of possibilities will arise for their rendezvous with friendly submarines or other aircraft or for their landing and internment in neutral territory. So long as the principle is established that the plane itself need not be salvaged, an enormous extension of range results, and that extension need not be greatly affected by plans for the rescue of the crew. One must add that there are also other possibilities which may be developed for extending the range of existing aircraft, as, for example, by refueling in flight.

With these considerations in mind, we may contemplate the facts that a B-29 has made a nonstop flight of 8,200 statute miles, that bombers of considerably greater carrying capacity are far beyond the blueprint stage, and that Moscow is only 4,300 miles from the nearest United States air base in Maine. Certainly intercontinental warfare, at least as concerns strategic bombing, is not merely a possibility for the future. The seizure of advanced bases close to enemy territory may still present advantages for the successful use of the atomic bomb, but it is no longer an indispensable prerequisite to such use. And, depending upon its costs in men, resources, and especially time, the attempt to seize such bases as a preliminary to the use of the bomb may well prove a strategy of waste.

The character of the adaptation required of the military services generally under the situation we are postulating is governed, first, by the fact that the atomic bomb and the system for delivering it are indisputably the major or "decisive" arm and, second, by the absence of any grave threat of an atomic counterblow. The first of these factors will demand not only that the mechanics of atomic attack will receive overriding priority in development and resources but also that the services not directly concerned with those mechanics nevertheless be oriented toward a strategy which recognizes the atomic bomb as the decisive weapon. Such orientation would involve, among other things, great emphasis on mobility of troops, in order that advantages gained by initial use of the atomic bomb may be promptly exploited. The second factor, in so far as it can be relied upon as a reality (which would depend mostly on the character of our intelligence), would give our services the freedom of action necessary for their proper orientation. That freedom can never be complete, since, whatever the excellence of our intelligence, we would never be justified in proceeding exclusively on the assumption that the enemy had no atomic bombs or means of delivering them.

A strategy which gives first place to offensive use of the atomic bomb implies an implementing but by no means inferior role for the navy and ground forces. For one thing, the amount of resources which the system of atomic attack can absorb will always be ruled by the number of atomic bombs in hand. Then there is the matter of diminishing returns in the use of any one weapon however powerful, and the atomic bomb might by its very successes quickly put itself into a subordinate role. That is exactly what happened to the American submarine in the latter stages of the Pacific war, when the lack of ship targets as a result largely of our previous submarine successes caused us to cut back our submarine-building program. Finally, the fact that a weapon is deemed decisive does not in military parlance mean that it is necessarily conclusive. The enemy may continue to resist though his cities be devastated, and, if a final conclusion to the business is desired, his territory may have to be invaded and occupied. Or his armies may have to be driven out of countries which they have occupied. In any case, large ground, sea, and air operations extending over months or even years of time might have to be undertaken.

A word should be added about the use of very-long-range rockets as vehicles for the atomic bomb. Some scientists and engineers in the field of guided missiles insist that, before we can have an accurately guided rocket of two or three thousand miles' range, such revolutionary developments are necessary that it is safe to presume that the event is at least twenty-five years away. Others among their colleagues argue that the length of time required depends largely upon the effort put into the job and that a fraction of the amount of effort that went into the Manhattan District Project would bring the result much sooner. Certainly the atomic bomb is a powerful enough weapon to warrant a good deal of research and development upon special vehicles for its conveyance. But those special vehicles need not take the form of rockets. Jet-propelled bombers, perhaps reaching supersonic speeds, would be difficult enough for any defense to cope with, and they are certainly much closer in time and would probably be much more reliable than three-thousand-mile rockets of the V-2 type.

Moreover, it must be remembered that the V-2 in our hands in 1944–45 would not have been nearly so useful to us as it was to the Germans. To us, with our overwhelming air superiority, it would have been a rather wasteful means of adding to our air bombardment strength. To the Germans at the time it was almost the only means of hitting back. The fact that it had certain advantages over aircraft is by no means unimportant, but it would be wrong to conclude, as some senior officers have concluded, that the effective use of atomic bombs must await a development in rockets which happens to be comfortably far off.[8]

Another question which arises is whether we would use the atomic bomb at all in another war if we were confident that we had a monopoly. To be sure, monopoly conditions would give us a certain freedom of choice in this matter which would probably be absent if the enemy too had a substantial number of atomic bombs. But, apart from the historical fact that we used the bombs against Japan when we had only two in hand and when we recognized that Japan was already defeated, there is another factor bearing on this question.

8. On this point see the paper entitled "U.S. Navy Thinking on the Atomic Bomb," in the already cited "Public Affairs Bulletin," No. 55, pp. 30–33; see also the relevant comments in the "Compiler's Critique on U.S. Navy Views," in the same bulletin, pp. 42–48. Some senior naval officers interviewed appeared to believe that the bombing plane was too "unreliable" a vehicle for the atomic bomb and that the development of a very-long-range rocket capable of carrying it lay in the distant future. The *reductio ad absurdum* of this argument is too obvious.

So long as the number of atomic bombs in our arsenal is small, their existence has relatively little influence on the composition and strategy of our armed services. In that case we can choose whether or not to use them in the event of war. But the latitude of choice tends to narrow as the number grows. For if the possession of a large number of bombs demands that all our armed services orient themselves toward an atomic offensive strategy, they must either carry out that orientation (in which case they would not be well prepared to fight a great nonatomic war) or pay heavy forfeit in the effectiveness of the bombs available. In other words, we cannot forever go on planning for two drastically different kinds of large-scale war. Considerations of economy and of getting the most possible fighting strength out of our military resources will dictate that we make up our minds at an early date whether or not we will use the bombs in war and adjust accordingly. There is not much doubt about what that decision will be, especially since the general expectation is that—failing the setting-up of an effective international control system—our major rival will begin to make atomic bombs within the next ten to twenty years.

AMERICAN SUPERIORITY UNDER POSTMONOPOLY CONDITIONS

Situation (3): the end of American monopoly, but with the United States still enjoying a large margin of superiority over its major rival both in atomic bombs and in the means of delivering them.—This situation has been virtually ignored in the debate on the strategic implications of the atomic bomb, yet it is one which will almost certainly endure for a long time after the Soviet Union produces its first bomb. There are several factors supporting this estimate.

First, there is some reason to believe that the amount of uranium and thorium available in the world for the manufacture of atomic bombs is much more limited than was being assumed two years ago, and the deposits available are much more accessible to the United States than to the Soviet Union. Hanson Baldwin was probably reflecting informed and heretofore confidential opinion when he made the following observations in the *New York Times* for November 9, 1947: "Responsible Government authorities have made a reassessment of atomic possibilities, short-term and long-term, in the past two years and a dramatic change in attitude toward the short-term future has resulted. Two years ago atomic scientists were talking glibly of 10,000 atomic bombs as if they were an accomplished fact; we were assured repeatedly that Russia could catch up and overtake the United States in short order. . . . Today more sober judgment has intervened. . . . We know, too, that atomic bomb production is not a rapid and easy process, and that for a very long time to come the numbers available to us will be limited, and they will be far more limited to the Russians." Earlier in the same article Baldwin makes the following statement: "But it seems probable that the U.S.S.R. does not now have—although she may be able to find and develop at some future time—sufficient quantities of uranium to build many bombs. Unless she can get access to more uranium she probably will not be able to turn out bombs at a production rate in any way comparable to our own. In other words, we seemingly have almost a monopoly today on the *known* important sources of uranium." Thus, even apart from the matter of the important head start which we have, and which is likely to grow much greater before the Soviet Union produces its first bomb, the ultimate maximum production in that country is by no means likely to compare with our own ultimate maximum production.

We need only remember that the three most important known deposits of uranium lie in Canada, the Belgian Congo, and the United States, and that the fourth major deposit—in Czechoslovakia—is far less rich than any of the other three, to get a conception of the relative accessibility of uranium as between the United States and the Soviet Union. In thorium the situation is not far different, the two major known deposits being in Brazil and in India.

Second, the enormous technological lead which the United States has over the Soviet Union and which shows no immediate signs of diminishing is bound to mean a great potential advantage for the United States in the design of the instruments for using the atomic bomb. The atomic bomb by itself has no military utility. It must be delivered to the target in some kind of vehicle which, unless it is a free-flying rocket, is subject to various kinds of attack. Marked superiority in the vehicle or in the means of shooting down the enemy's vehicles may be no less important than superiority in numbers of bombs. Especially if those several types of superiority are concentrated on the same side, the disparity in atomic fighting power may be sufficient to warrant comparison with outright monopoly.

The Soviet Union has been able, with the assistance of German technicians, to build several types of jet-propelled fighters, and she has also built several large bombers patterned after our B-29, some models of which were impounded by her during the war. But a few

German technicians are not going to make the difference between a backward technology and an eagerly progressive one. Our lead in types of aircraft, in the ordnance of combat aviation, and in anti-aircraft material should, or rather *could*, be as great during the next twenty years as it was in the recent war. The only question is whether we will make the necessary effort to keep in the lead in our military technology. That the Soviet Union will spare no effort within her capabilities to overtake us goes without saying.

How do the military characteristics of situation (3) differ from those of the situation described in the immediately preceding pages? We must first acknowledge that situation (3) covers a wide range of possibilities, shading from near-monopoly position, on the one hand, to insignificant superiority, on the other. But so long as we are stipulating an *important* superiority both in bombs and in the instruments for using them, our problem is much simplified.

As concerns the offensive use of the atomic bomb itself, the same considerations which operated in situation (2) will tend to prevail here as well. The fact that the enemy possesses *some* atomic bombs may, on the one hand, put a greater urgency upon our using those we have in order to anticipate his attack and to weaken the potential strength of that attack; or it may, on the other hand, cause us to hold our bombs as a threat to induce him to withhold his. The latter procedure would, of course, nullify the offensive significance of our superiority unless our plan was to withhold our bombs only until the enemy was no longer in a position to use his effectively.

The fact that the enemy has some bombs will, however, greatly affect the offensive use of our forces other than those directly concerned with atomic warfare. The most obvious example is to be found in the case of the amphibious operation. It has been often enough observed that the Germans would not have needed very many atomic bombs utterly to disrupt and frustrate our Normandy landing in 1944. Our offensive strategy will have to be careful to avoid tactical concentrations of force in markedly exposed places. That is much more easily said than done, since the essence of offensive power has always been assumed to lie in the concentration of superior force at the appropriate place. In fact, the orthodox textbooks on strategy have usually elevated the idea of concentration to the status of a basic principle and have spoken of the "principle of concentration" as a corollary to the "principle of the offensive." The solution to this dilemma, and some solution will no doubt be found under any given set of circumstances, will probably emphasize the distinction between tactical and strategic concentration. A force can be strategically concentrated while dispersed over a considerable amount of space, so long as its components can work together to effect a common end and can achieve temporary tactical concentrations if need be. There is still the dilemma that tactical concentrations may on occasion be necessary, as they have been in the past, but no doubt some ways can be found of achieving the degree of concentration necessary to a tactical end while minimizing the vulnerability of that concentration to atomic-bomb attack. These are problems to be worked out in the future, and they can usually be worked out satisfactorily only with a given set of circumstances pertaining to a particular campaign at a given point of time. On the other hand, it is by no means too early to begin thinking about some of the basic issues involved. It is not too early, for example, for our strategists to start rethinking the campaigns of the recent war with the assumption that the enemy had had a few atomic bombs to use at critical places. Some very important conclusions would no doubt follow from such exercises.

It is on the defensive side that the most significant changes take place. The most important statement in this respect is to be found in the War Department paper previously cited: "The atomic bomb, primarily an offensive weapon, serves to emphasize the principle that only by offensive action can victory be attained. However, the development of the atomic bomb by other nations requires that the U.S. adopt a principle of strategy in seeming conflict with the fundamental importance of offensive effort. *We must devote a higher percentage of our national resources than ever before to the measures we take for defense.* We must do this in order to insure that we retain the capability of delivering effective offensive effort."[9]

This statement is contained in a paper which declares at the outset that it is considering in the main a situation in the future when other nations besides the United States possess "significant quantities" of atomic bombs. However, it applies at least as cogently in a situation where the enemy has only a very small number of bombs, for two reasons: (1) even a very few bombs—fewer than twenty, for example—could accomplish demoralization and perhaps fatal disruption in an America quite unprepared to cope with them, and (2) the kind of defenses described in the War Department paper make more

9. *Op. cit.*, pp. 77–78.

sense, in terms of probable accomplishment, against an attack confined to a very limited number of bombs than they would against an attack involving hundreds of bombs.

The kind of defenses alluded to by the War Department paper might be summarized as comprising the following: defense against the vehicles of atomic attack (i.e., aircraft or guided missiles) through a development of devices comparable to those used against air attack in the recent war (air-fighter interception plus antiaircraft missiles plus radar detection); defense against the air-borne and sea-borne invasion forces which might seek to capitalize on the disruption caused by the attack (hardly a likely contingency where we are positing great atomic superiority on our side); readiness for instant retaliation; and a very modest amount of selective dispersion of vital industries (the paper is quite explicit and emphatic on the point that any wholesale dispersion of American cities is wholly out of the question).

THE SECURITY PROBLEM IN THE EVENT OF LOSS OF ATOMIC SUPERIORITY

Situation (4): the end not only of monopoly but also of significant American superiority.—This is the "all-out" atomic war upon which most of the prognosticators have been concentrating their attention. It might also be called the "impossible war," especially if a large number of atomic bombs were presupposed on both sides. It would be impossible to fight by any traditional use of traditional arms, and the cost even to the victor would be greater than that paid by any vanquished country in history. Yet the "impossible" war might have to be fought, partly because real threat of instant retaliation is the most important single defense under a situation of bilateral or multilateral distribution of large numbers of bombs, and partly because there is no precedent in history for supposing that large and proud nations will go on yielding forever to a rival whose strength, while terrible, is not overwhelmingly superior. The burdens on diplomacy for avoiding war under the conditions we are postulating are unimaginable, but the task is incomparably important. But the only thing that will keep diplomacy from breaking down ultimately is the conviction *on all sides* that war is far too horrible even to be contemplated. And the great dilemma is that that conviction can be sustained only by our making every possible effort to prepare for war and thus to engage in it if need be.

The condition of no-monopoly–no-superiority requires the least discussion, not only because it is most remote in time (and perhaps probability), but also because most of the meaningful ideas on the subject thus far expressed have already been gathered together in two or three quite brief and easily accessible pieces.[10]

To make a brief exposition even briefer, these ideas seem to the present writer to boil down to the following basic conclusions.

First, since the chief "defense"—in the sense that it is the chief hope of avoiding war under the postulated conditions—lies in the threat of instant retaliation in kind in case of atomic attack, the provision of such means of instant retaliation must have complete and overriding priority. That means, among other things, that the organization responsible for such retaliation must be as far as possible isolated not only from the rest of the national community but also from the rest of the armed forces. It must be insulated from the effects of the catastrophe and horror which the enemy's initial attack will have visited upon our cities. In short, it must have as much freedom as it is humanly possible to provide for it to carry out its appointed task.

Second, not only must mobilization be complete or nearly so at the very outset of hostilities, but the means of fighting too must be stock-piled in a finished state. The situation will demand not a stock-piling of raw materials—for the processing of which there will be neither time nor facilities—but a stock-piling of finished commodities. There is little room under these conditions for planning which presumes a great expansion of war production after hostilities or projects campaigns involving heavy and continuing reliance upon a large and well-integrated industry, because the basis of such reliance will have quickly dissolved into thin but radioactive air. Great navies will not roam the seas in the absence of an industrial base to keep them at sea, nor will great armies take the field. The fighting will be done by small but mobile forces operating from autonomous and previously provided sources of supply.

Third, every *feasible* means of dispersion of populations and of industry will have to be carried out in advance. Admittedly the maxi-

10. See especially my two chapters, entitled "War in the Atomic Age" and "Implications for Military Policy," in *The Absolute Weapon, Atomic Power and World Order*, ed. Bernard Brodie (New York: Harcourt, Brace & Co., 1946); also the already cited "Public Affairs Bulletin," No. 55, especially the War Department paper contained in it; see also Ansley Coale, *The Problem of Reducing Vulnerability to Atomic Bombs* (Princeton, 1947).

mum feasible amount is not likely to mean a wholesale dispersion of our cities.

Fourth, it goes without saying that the provision of a system for detecting and attacking the enemy vehicles of atomic attack has a priority second only to that of providing means of retaliation. It fails to have first priority only because it is not presently conceivable that a defense against the air vehicles of the future carrying large numbers of atomic bombs will be so successful as to prevent the large-scale destruction of our cities. If it becomes conceivable through new developments, then clearly the system of defense has priority over everything, and offensive forces will then be able to operate from a hinterland representing something other than complete ruin. But under those circumstances we would really be postulating situation (3), already described, rather than situation (4). While it is improbable that the most advanced form of defense will be adequate to cope with the most advanced form of offense, it may be less improbable over the next twenty years that American methods of defense will be adequate to cope with Soviet offense.

To be sure, the no-monopoly–no-superiority condition might be expressed with a small number of bombs on both sides, in which case the situation is closest to that described under (1)—but that condition could arise only if a previously effective international control scheme suddenly collapsed. On the other hand, if we go on building bombs, and if the Russians later overtake us, it is not likely that at that time the number in the hands of either party will be small.

For logical completeness we should add another situation, that is, No. 3 in reverse: the Soviet Union enjoying a large margin of superiority both in atomic bombs and in the means of delivering them. It is not squeamishness but simply a disinclination to deal with futility on which we base our refusal to be logically complete.

What adjustments do the propositions suggested above indicate for our over-all national policy? We have, first of all, to consider the consequences of the fact that in a world armed with substantial numbers of atomic bombs the decisive phase of a war between great powers is bound to be short. That will mean an accent, which at least for the United States will be unprecedented, not merely upon preparedness in the old sense of the term—which involved mainly provision for great expansion of the military services and of military production after the outbreak of hostilities—but upon having a military establishment ready to shift to a war footing on very short notice.

We are already witnessing the stirrings of that recognition in the measures recently adopted to institute a peacetime draft and to build up our air force to seventy groups. These measures have been, to be sure, markedly stimulated by our current difficulties with the Soviet Union, but those difficulties have probably served merely to hasten an adjustment which was inevitable in any case. When and if we enter a happy period of relatively easy relations between the Soviets and ourselves, we can count upon our military leaders to carry out their unquestioned duty of reminding us that we are after all living in an age of atomic bombs.

This country has long been accustomed to the policy of having at least one branch of the armed services, the navy, ready at least in theory to assume a war footing in short notice. The fact that the emphasis now shifts to the air forces—in fact, the atomic bomb threatens to deprive the navy of most of its historic functions—makes a great deal of difference in the degree of effort necessary to maintain what is loosely termed "preparedness." In the first place, the rate of obsolescence of the basic equipment of the navy—that is, the warships themselves—has for the last forty years been far lower than the recent and current rate of obsolescence of aircraft. That, of course, gives some indication of mounting costs. Coupled with that, and more important, is the fact that the atomic bomb has for the first time destroyed the invulnerability of the United States to direct air attack from the Eurasian continent. To be sure, there were bombs before the atomic bomb and aircraft which were steadily increasing in potential range, but no reasonably conceivable development of aircraft, at least along principles now known, would have made such attack a practical proposition on a sustained basis so long as one had to use chemical bombs. It requires only a brief digression to indicate why.

The problem of very-long-range bombing has never been simply that of getting a few bombs delivered to the maximum possible distance. Except for purely demonstration purposes (such as the Doolittle raid on Tokyo and our first B-29 raid on the same city from bases in China), it has meant carrying *enough* bombs per sortie to make militarily worth while the cost of the sortie. And since costs tend to rise with distance by something comparable to a geometrical progression, the barrier to extreme-range bombing has been that the necessity for carrying large payloads (of chemical bombs) mounts most rapidly just as the physical feasibility of doing so drops drastically. With an atomic bomb, however, there is little question of the sortie paying for itself at whatever distance it is physically possible to deliver it. Moreover, whatever developments the bomb may undergo, there is no necessity for its ever weighing more than either the Hiroshima or the Nagasaki bomb. Thus, any improvement in the weight-carrying capacity of aircraft can be devoted entirely to the carriage of more fuel for either greater range or speed or both. There is no necessity for proportionately increasing the bomb load. Besides, as we have already noted, the fact that much larger costs can be accepted for sorties with atomic bombs than for sorties with chemical bombs means that in the former case the aircraft need not be retrieved, while in the latter case there must be a high percentage of recovery.

What do these new factors indicate concerning the future costs of military preparedness? Oddly enough, there is little direct correlation historically between the rate of innovation in weapons and the size of military budgets. For example, between 1808 and 1893, at a time when the character of the warship was changing at a fantastic rate—when ships were actually becoming obsolete before they were completed relative to new ships already under construction—the naval budget for Great Britain remained practically stationary at a figure of about eleven million pounds. If that figure is related to the rising national income during that time, we see that the proportion of the national wealth spent on naval security for Britain was rapidly diminishing—and that during the period when the cost of the individual ship was expanding most rapidly. What are the reasons for that? Of course the times were relatively pacific, but it was also true that the changes then ensuing were not fundamentally altering the basic premises of degree of national security and of the duration of wars. As long as Britain retained superiority on the seas against other powers, which she could do with the new weapons as well as with the old, she did not have to worry about being overwhelmed in the first days or weeks of war.

The atomic bomb, on the contrary, is bound to result, as it already has, in increased costs of military security. That is something to be perturbed about, unquestionably, but we should not assume that there is no roof to those increased costs. There are certain important restraining factors. We have already noticed in Congress, during the recent debate on the increase of the armed forces, a very decided reluctance to appropriate sums which threatened to cause a deficit in the national budget. Congress quite properly feels that deficit financing is not appropriate for times of boom. Thus, while Congress approved by overwhelming vote the principle of a seventy-group air force, it rejected the contention of Secretary Forrestal that an increase in air groups required also a proportionate increase in the army and navy involving a total additional cost of fifteen or sixteen billion dollars.

Historians have dwelt on the scale of the armament races preceding the two world wars, usually without observing that the scale is partly a question of the point of view. In each case the extent of the arming turned out with most the belligerents to be relatively small in comparison to the expansion of the war period itself. We observe, in other words, a certain pronounced and effective reluctance to strain the national economy overmuch even when war appears imminent. It is characteristic of wartime economies that many kinds of production for civilian consumption are deferred and that expenditures creating huge inflationary pressures are made as a matter of course. In both cases the abnormality is accepted largely because it is deemed by the population to be temporary. Dictatorships and democracies differ only in degree but not fundamentally in kind in the limits of toleration accorded to advances in the permanent level of military budgets. Despite the recent great rise in the United States military appropriations, the American people have not yet in their entire history accepted in peacetime any increase that could be deemed to have a clear and immediate depressing effect upon their standard of living. That does not argue that they will never do so in the future. But it does suggest the existence of powerful inhibiting forces acting to limit the rate of growth of military expenditures.

In that connection we have heard much of the business of dispersing our cities—a matter which has already been alluded to in the foregoing pages. Such dispersion would have to be accomplished within the next twenty years at most if it is to keep pace with the development of the need. Within such a period a wholesale dispersion of our industries and populations would be physically if not economically impossible. Much of the wealth of this country exists in the form of fixed and sunk capital and therefore, by definition, not subject to removal. Second, one might venture to estimate that such dispersion would probably be militarily improvident even if it were possible. A great many fighter planes could be provided with what it would cost to disperse one moderate-sized city. Third, if our intuitions about how people feel about those things are anywhere near correct, it would in any case be vigorously resisted. There is a good margin for dispersion which would be minor in scale but probably important in quality, and commitment to such dispersion is about as far as one can expect our government will ever go, if indeed it goes that far.

In venturing such a prediction, one must make due allowance for the excitement which will prevail in this country when the conviction settles upon it that the Soviet Union is producing atomic bombs. Measures not otherwise imaginable might then become entirely feasible. The main question is whether the outlet for the perturbation will take the form of extravagance in defense (including wholesale dispersion) or a will to aggression. In that connection we must bear in mind the observation made above that on the day the Soviet Union makes its first atomic bomb the United States will have many more than it does now. Depending upon when that situation occurs, the promptness with which the realization of it is communicated to the American people, and the current state of relations with the Soviet Union, the psychology of "preventive war" might become a much more difficult one to suppress than it appears to be at present. On the other hand, it is equally conceivable that the capacity of the human animal for inertia in the face of clear and present danger will again be demonstrated. The very incomprehensibility of the potential catastrophe inherent in the atomic bomb may well make easier the development of the habit of living with it.

MODERN TECHNOLOGY AND THE
WORLD ORDER

By QUINCY WRIGHT

THE NATURE OF THE WORLD ORDER

THE world order at any moment consists of four aspects which may be described by the words "communication," "standardization," "co-operation," and "organization." A system of communication and transport brings the major groups of the world and the individuals which compose them into more or less contact with one another. Patterns of assumption, evaluation, interpretation, behavior, and reaction which the members of all these groups mutually understand and expect provide an adequate or inadequate basis for adjusting relations, co-operating to common ends, and dealing with conflicts. A larger or smaller body of loyalties, values, purposes, and objectives are shared and, in varying measure, realized by common or separate effort. Institutions, organizations, and procedures to greater or lesser extent formalize, regulate, and control co-operative and oppositional activities.

Each of these aspects of the world order may be measured according to its magnitude and rate of change. Thus, one may say of any two groups or of all the groups in the world order that they communicate with one another more or less; that they are standardized considerably or slightly; that they co-operate with one another much or little; that they are organized effectively or ineffectively. Each of these variables may be increasing or decreasing, and it may be doing so rapidly or slowly. Obviously, such characterizations are seldom applicable uniformly throughout the world. Magnitude and direction and rate of change may vary among pairs of groups or in regions or in respect to particular functions.[1]

1. See *The World Community*, ed. Q. Wright (Chicago: University of Chicago Press, 1948), especially chap. iv by Margaret Mead on "World Culture." Miss Mead believes that the world community would be best developed if varied cultures become complementary rather than alike in a more inclusive world culture. Crane Brinton (*From Many One* [Cambridge: Harvard University Press, 1948]) illustrates the process of subordinating independent groups to a larger whole in the formation of the Roman Empire and the French kingdom. He attributes importance to the regularity of communications from the center to the parts, the development of general loyalty to the symbolic ruler, and the activity of a centrally instructed administrative élite. Standardization of the cultures of the member-groups he considers of lesser importance in building these societies.

These variables are not entirely independent. Increasing communication between groups tends to standardize their members and perhaps in the long run to increase their disposition to co-operate and to subordinate themselves to a single organization. Increasing organization may increase the other variables. In so far as all aspects of the world order increase together, we may say that the solidarity or integration of the world is increasing. Solidarity is perhaps used more commonly to refer to the intangible aspects of group development—standardization and co-operation—while integration is used to refer to the tangible aspects—communication and organization.

These variables, however, manifest considerable independence. Increasing communication between groups may cause reactions of opposition, as the result of which each group develops its traditional policies, cultural patterns, and institutions with increasing vigor in an effort to counteract the normal standardizing and integrating effect of increasing contact. Groups may fear the development of interdependence and take measures to preserve their independence.

The character of the world order, or indeed of any social order, may therefore be defined in terms of the magnitude of these variables at any moment, the lags and leads of one compared with another, and their directions and rates of change. Thus it may be difficult to say at any moment whether the world order is increasing or decreasing in solidarity and integration.

Prior to the discoveries of the late fifteenth century, it could hardly be said that there was any world order at all. Large groups inhabiting separated parts of the world, such as the Mayas, the Incas, the Chinese, the Indians, and the Europeans, had practically no contact at all. There was nothing that could be described as standardization, co-operation, or organization among them.

Since that time contact has developed among all peoples through trade, missionary enterprise, diplomacy, war, conquest, administration, cultural exchange, postal and telecommunication, news-reporting, and broadcasting. With such contacts, standardization, co-operation, and organization have tended to increase. Although history records the unevenness and irregularity of this development, the general trend appears to have been toward a more interconnected, interdependent, integrated, standardized, and organized world order.

Along with this shrinking of the world and the probable increase in its solidarity have come general increases in population, in wealth, and in literacy. The process, however, has been punctuated by wars of increasing destructiveness and has been marred by increasing restiveness of peoples that endure conditions of life which are permanently or temporarily inferior to those enjoyed by people elsewhere.

These factors, the increasing frequency and destructiveness of war and the increasing size and violence of revolutionary movements, threaten to modify the trend of the past few centuries and suggest that changes may be in progress as great as those of the fifth and fifteenth centuries, often referred to as transitions from one civilization to another.

It would be generally agreed that the new technology, which began in Europe with the development of clocks, the compass, and water- and windmills in the late Middle Ages and which was stimulated by the development of gunpowder, printing, double-entry bookkeeping, and astronomy in the fifteenth century, had much to do with this trend of the world order.[2] Interest in natural science, economics, and war and the development of mechanics, chemistry, and electronics led to the steam engine, the steamboat, the locomotive, the breach-loading rifle, the machine gun, the armored warship, the internal combustion engine, the electric motor, the motor vehicle, the airplane, the telegraph, the telephone, the radio, radar, the submarine, the tank, high explosives, torpedoes and mines, toxic gases, and the atomic bomb.

The speed of invention has accelerated, and the world order has also changed with increasing speed. While the general trend has apparently been toward more interdependence of the parts of the world order and toward more standardization, co-operation, and organization of its people, opposite tendencies of disintegration, differentiation, and disorganization have always been apparent because of the even greater speed with which the nation-states have increased in solidarity and integration. In recent years the development of totalitarian states has presented the extraordinary spectacle of a world order moving toward unity and toward chaos at the same time, a condition popularly characterized by the phrase "one world or none."[3]

THE RELATION OF TECHNOLOGY AND OPINION

A more precise description of the role of invention and technology in this process may contribute to both prediction and control. That

2. Q. Wright, *A Study of War* (2 vols.; Chicago: University of Chicago Press, 1942), I, 606 ff.

3. *Ibid.*, chaps. viii and xiv.

role is by no means a simple one. The world order has at any moment a certain degree of solidarity because of the relations of its component and constituent groups, but this degree of solidarity is continually changing in time because of the uneven increases or decreases in the contact, standardization, co-operation, and organization of people within and among these groups. The behavior of this complicated and changing world order is greatly influenced, on the one hand, by inventions and, on the other hand, by opinions. Different schools of historical interpretation have emphasized one or the other of these influences. Materialists emphasize invention, technology, resources, and science, while idealists emphasize opinions, wants, policies, and faiths. It would seem, however, that both new instruments and new ideas enter into the process of social change, just as, according to the psychoanalysts, both the reality and the wish principle are necessary to explain individual behavior.

Technology cannot be said to *determine* the character of the world order. The effect of a particular technological invention or importation upon a particular social order depends upon the way in which it is utilized, and that utilization is in large measure influenced by the values and the culture of the social order. An invention provides means by which wants may be satisfied and opinions realized. These wants and opinions spring from many sources: traditional beliefs, philosophical interpretations, religious inspirations, and social policies which have developed in the culture.

Neither do opinions, wants, policies, ideals, or ideologies *determine* the character of a social order. Their effect in a particular social order depends in considerable degree upon the means for their realization which are made available in the existing culture.

The effect, therefore, of both technological inventions and social aspirations depends upon the characteristics of the culture in the social order under consideration. In one culture a particular invention or a particular social idea will be absorbed and utilized immediately; in another it will pass like water off a duck's back. The differential receptiveness of primitive peoples to guns and to Bibles has often been noted. It is to be observed, however, that inventions and opinions influence one another. Students of inventions have recognized that they do not emerge suddenly and accidentally. They emerge where a vigorous social demand is accompanied by sufficient technological conditions. When the demand and the conditions exist, the invention is often made independently by several people.[4] Similarly, students of social and political ideas have recognized that the emergence of social demands and opinions other than desire for the barest needs of physical life are in considerable measure conditioned by the state of technology. Unless the means of realization are on the horizon, ideas will not spread. One can, for example, find occasional expressions of the desire of man to fly in documents of ancient Chinese, Indian, and classic cultures, as well as those of more recent civilizations; but, until the internal combustion engine had been invented, these ideas did not attract wide interest.[5]

Thus wants and inventions develop hand in hand. Technological development leads to new wants, and new wants stimulate new inventions. Quantitatively, this reciprocal process tends to accelerate the rate of change, and, qualitatively, it tends to emphasize those wants susceptible of satisfaction by mechanical gadgets. Civilization tends to move with increasing speed from an "ideational" to a "sensate" emphasis until the ideal bases of solidarity are so undermined that the civilization breaks up.[6]

The increasing rate of change which during the past century has rapidly rendered technological skills obsolete and required continuous adaptation of institutions and principles to new technological conditions has had profound effects on education and on modes of social control. Tradition which in the past played a major role in education, and custom which in the past was the major social control, are today of less influence than ever before. Education pays ever more attention to science and less to the classics. Social control relies ever more on public administration guided by legislation reflecting prevailing public opinion and less on judicial procedures guided by common law based on time-honored precedents and principles. Both national and international legislation tend to operate by the method of formulating and administering policy rather than by the method of deciding cases in accord with principles of "natural justice." As a result, restrictions on the means utilized for giving effect to policy, whether propaganda or coercion, reward or punishment, are less observed. Any means, however barbarous or novel, will be used if it appears suitable for achieving the end sought.

4. J. Rossman, *The Psychology of the Inventor* (Washington, D.C., 1931); S. C. Gilfillan *The Sociology of Invention* (Chicago, 1937).

5. Berthold Laufer, *The Prehistory of Aviation* ("Field Museum Anthropological Series," Vol. XVIII [Chicago, 1928]).

6. Pitirim Sorokin, *Social and Cultural Dynamics* (New York, 1937), I, 404; Arnold J. Toynbee, *A Study of History* (Oxford, 1934), I, 62 ff.

The emphasis upon the satisfaction of material needs—food, clothing, housing—as prime values, because they are ones which invention and technology may satisfy, has influenced the subject matter of national and international legislation and has probably reduced the relative importance in modern civilization of the fine arts, individual liberty, moral moderation, and historical perspective. Recent bills of rights, both national and international, have given a far greater importance to economic and social rights, such as the right to work, the right to adequate conditions of work, and the right to social security, than did the bills of rights of the eighteenth century. The latter emphasized freedoms of religion, speech, and press and moderations of criminal and civil procedure.

The tendency to believe that the end justifies the means and that material ends are paramount has been especially noted in the conduct of war. Rules of war expressive of the virtues of moderation and the principles of humanity even in dealing with the enemy have been less and less observed in recent wars. Prisoners of war have been slaughtered or subjected to unusual hardships, civilians in occupied areas have been massacred wholesale, and cities have been destroyed. A recent military writer who contributed greatly to the development of the tank, and who completed his book before the destruction of Hiroshima by an atomic bomb, compared the massacre of Magdeburg in 1631 with the even greater destruction of life and property in Hamburg in 1943. He comments: "The one great difference between these two atrocities is that, in 1631, the massacre of Magdeburg sent a thrill of horror throughout Christendom, whereas in 1943, the massacre of Hamburg was received by acclamation in England as had the massacre of Coventry in 1940 in Germany. In the Thirty Years' War, when it was suggested to Gustavus Adolphus that he should demolish the Ducal Palace in Munich, not only did he reject the advice with indignation, but he took particular care to preserve it. Today that palace is a rubble heap." This writer continues: "When we think it out, it is the inventive genius of man which has obliterated his sense of moral values. From the javelin and the arrow to the superfortress and the rocket bomb, the very power to destroy, first slowly and then at terrific speed, has intoxicated man. From out the first flint axe and bended bow has at length emerged a Frankenstein monster—the inventiveness of today—that is destroying man's own work, his own culture, his own civilization, his past, his present, and his future."[7]

7. Major General J. F. C. Fuller, *Armament and History* (New York, 1945), pp. xiii–xiv.

This view may be exaggerated. It emphasizes, however, one relationship between invention and civilization.

DEVELOPMENT OF THE MODERN WORLD ORDER

The relations of technology and solidarity can perhaps be illustrated more easily in the history of the world order than in that of smaller communities, because the world order has been less integrated and fewer inventions have been significant in its development.

The modern world order has been characterized by the relative independence of its geographically defined component groups and the relative importance of these groups as compared with functional groups.

In the Middle Ages and earlier, the American, Asiatic, and European civilizations were so completely separated from one another that it was hardly possible to speak of a world order at all. Each civilization constituted an independent international order. European Christendom, which historically took the initiative in establishing the modern world order, was divided into thousands of manors, free cities, principalities, and kingdoms, united by a feudal hierarchy, theoretically topped by the pope and the emperor. The authority of the pope was more than theoretical, because the clergy, bound to him by official loyalty as well as by hierarchical authority, functioned in every village, town, and city. The functional group of the clergy and, in less degree, the functional groups of merchant guilds and mercantile leagues at times exceeded in importance the geographical groups constituted by the kingdoms and principalities.

The reduction of the prestige and the authority of the pope and the emperor by the schisms of the late Middle Ages, the rise of the power of the monarchs, utilizing gunpowder to batter down feudal castles and the printing press to create a consciousness of national languages, loyalties, and customs, increased the importance of the geographically defined states. The movements known as the Renaissance and the Reformation were stimulated by and contributed to this geographical division of Europe, formally recognized in the Peace of Westphalia, which ended the Thirty Years' War in 1648. Each state was recognized as sovereign in law, and its continued existence as a geographical, administrative, and legal unity was regarded as a major value, first, by its ruler and, later, as the sentiment of nationalism developed, by all its population. That existence depended upon military self-help. Thus international politics was power politics, and stability could result only from a balance arising from policies pur-

sued by each state to oppose any one of their number which theat-
ened to become so powerful as to engulf its neighbors.[8]

Each state had an interest in such a threat which varied (so long as
the exertion of military power was seriously hampered by strategic
distance) in proportion to its distance from the threatening state. It
did not take great intelligence to see that, if a state engulfed its neighbor, it would be in a better position to engulf its next neighbor, and
presently universal empire would develop in which all would lose
their independence, as they had by the conquests of Rome. Such a
process was always a possibility and progressed a considerable distance toward achievement under Louis XIV, Napoleon, the Kaiser,
and Hitler; but, with the initiative of Great Britain, secure on her
island base and wielding predominant sea power, the balance of
power was in each case restored. There was, however, a continuous
process of elimination of the smaller states by conquest or union.
Thus the number of European states which had been over four hundred at the time of Westphalia and three thousand a century before
had been reduced to less than a hundred at the time of the Conference
of Vienna and to only twenty at the time of the Berlin Conference of
1878. This number had been increased to thirty at the time of the
Versailles Conference, but more recently it has been reduced again.[9]

This system of power politics was extended by conquest and recognition to the Americas, Asia, and Africa during the centuries after
Westphalia, until, in the twentieth century, the entire land area of
the world was possessed under international law by some seventy
sovereign states, the boundaries of which were fairly clearly defined.

Along with this process of geographically defining the components
of the world order, certain institutions began to develop to hold them
together: first, occasional conferences and continuing consular and
diplomatic systems and, more recently, international administrative
unions and international political organizations.

Let us give consideration to the influence upon this development of
peace and war inventions.

INFLUENCE OF PEACE INVENTIONS

The invention and utilization of the gun and printing press exerted
an important influence, as has been noted, in wrecking the medieval
system, in developing the system of nation-states, and in spreading

8. Wright, *A Study of War*, I, 166 ff., 598 ff.
9. *Ibid.*, p. 215. According to Hans J. Morgenthau, the German Empire was reduced from
900 to 355 states in 1648, to 150 in 1803, to 36 in 1815, and to 24 in 1871 (*Review of Politics*, X
[April, 1948], 157).

that system throughout the world. Other inventions in the fields of transportation, communication, and production have been no less important. Such inventions in the latter part of the eighteenth century created the Industrial Revolution, after which inventions succeeded one another with accelerating pace throughout the nineteenth century. The steamboat, locomotive, motor vehicle, and airplane shrunk the world in respect to transportation time, while the post office, telegraph, telephone, and radio shrunk it in respect to communication time. The use of these inventions also had a tendency to distribute both population and techniques to all parts of the world. The contacts and economic interdependencies among the peoples of the various sections of the world greatly increased, but this did not immediately improve their relations. So long as each of these groups based its policy primarily on its own culture and traditions, increased contact tended to make controversy more frequent and conflicts of policy more difficult to solve peacefully.

In the long run, increase in contacts has tended to produce some cultural standardization, as manifested, for example, in the history of the United States, in which people in each of the states certainly resemble one another more in their beliefs and valuations than they did before the railroad, the newspaper, the airplane, the movie, and the radio had increased their contacts with one another and with identical ideas and expressions. Even in the world as a whole, these instruments have had some standardizing influence. The development of international law has also had a certain standardizing influence, particularly since that law has sought to extend its field into that of individual human rights and individual international crimes. Furthermore, administrative co-operation has been manifested in the activities of the numerous international unions and of the specialized organizations under the United Nations. There has even been some political organization, particularly in the League of Nations and the United Nations. But these influences have not been sufficient to modify the basic features of the state system.

The tendency toward greater world solidarity has, in fact, been retarded by the increased integration of each of the nation-states. This is a consequence in part of the inventions themselves. The first effect of improved facilities of transportation and communication has been to increase the use of these facilities locally, nationally, and regionally much more than among distant nations and between distant regions.[10] Furthermore, as national barriers to commercial and cultural infiltration were diminished with the progress of invention, nations tended to erect artificial barriers—protective tariffs, immigration laws, passport visas, censorships, and iron curtains—to preserve their economic invulnerability and their national distinctiveness. In addition, the demands of the underprivileged, and, in reply to them, the development of socialistic theories, intensified the meaning of national sovereignty by leading to national planning and governmentalization of industry and culture. Such policies developed further barriers to trade and cultural exchange.

States, therefore, still regard themselves as sovereign, and they practice that sovereignty more effectively than ever before. They seek to maintain the distinctiveness of their national characters, to formulate their policies to serve national ends, and to achieve their policies through their own instruments of domestic government, diplomacy, and war. The new technology has in fact increased the capacity and the will to develop national solidarity to such an extent that, in spite of increased international contacts, the solidarity of the world order is little greater than it was in the seventeenth and eighteenth centuries, when concepts of cosmopolitanism and natural law and declarations of individual freedom and equality were widely accepted.

The progress of invention in the production of foods, textiles, and housing, as well as other articles of common use, has both increased population and improved the living conditions of most people. This progress has also increased the demand for more inventions. The attention given to the pure sciences, because of the prestige which technology has achieved, has developed the bases for meeting that demand. The result has been that the rate of invention, and with it the rate of social change, in the principal states has greatly increased. This acceleration of history has meant that there has been less time to adjust to problems arising from international controversies and from the uneven rate of technical and economic development in different nations. Tensions therefore have increased, and there is more demand for speed in dealing with them. The latter demand tends to make peaceful adjustment less likely.

The inventions in production, the policies of national planning, and the unequal distribution of natural resources have together had

10. M. M. Willey and Stuart A. Rice, "The Agencies of Communication," in W. F. Ogburn (ed.), *Recent Social Trends* (New York, 1933), I, 217; Wright, *A Study of War*, I, 174–75.

the effect of augmenting national differences in living standards, while the communication inventions have increased general awareness of these differences. Demands by the underprivileged for better conditions have, therefore, increased in vigor. Such demands, when coupled with the considerable political influence acquired by the masses with the progress of democracy, and the accelerated capacity of technology to produce, have created conditions suitable for revolutionary ideas and practices. Such ideas and practices have been provided by Marxian theory and have taken root in large sections of the world.

Peacetime inventions have had an important influence upon the relative power position of states and therefore upon their policies and upon the stability of the balance of power. Manufacturing capacity; control of basic raw materials; large populations and internal transportation systems for mobilizing it; skill, education, and morale of population—all are important elements of political and military power under modern conditions of war. The industrial and transportation development of Germany, the United States, and Japan in the late nineteenth and early twentieth centuries increased their power position relative to that of France and Great Britain. The existence and exploitation of important oil resources improved the relative power position of the United States after the internal combustion engine came into use, and the existence of such resources in the Middle East made this area politically important. The widespread use of contraceptive devices first in France and then in western Europe and the United States tended to diminish the relative power position of these states compared with eastern Europe, Russia, and potentially Asia. "A nation," writes General Fuller, "faced by a stationary or falling birth rate intuitively fears war, because war hastens biological extinction."[11] On the other hand, improvements in the general economic level and in literacy in the West tended to increase the relative power position of these countries in the nineteenth century.

Public opinion within a nation is likely to become alarmed at losses of relative national prestige and power and to support aggressive policies to counteract such a development by expansion. On the other hand, national opinion may become complacent or domineering if the nation rapidly augments its national prestige and power and may support aggressive and imperialistic policies.

The progress of inventions, designed primarily for peaceful pur-

11. *Op. cit.*, p. 161.

poses, superimposed upon the state system, has, therefore, tended toward increasing controversy and tension in international relations and increasing demands for revolutionary change in the economically less favored parts of the world.

These conditions have been in a measure ameliorated by humanitarian and international movements and by the development of functional organizations to increase trade and cultural intercourse and to facilitate co-operation in the solution of welfare, health, agriculture, labor, and other problems. Such developments might have maintained the stability of the world order had it not been for the impact of war inventions.

INFLUENCE OF THE WAR INVENTIONS

From the Peace of Westphalia until the middle of the nineteenth century, military invention proceeded with improvements in artillery and hand arms augmenting the capacity of European states to make and maintain overseas empires. These inventions, however, had little effect upon the destructiveness of war or, among European states, upon the relative position of the offensive and the defensive. The revolutionary influence of the gun, in increasing offensive power against medieval fortresses and Swiss phalanxes, had been met by new methods of fortification and military discipline.[12] Louis XIV, with larger and better-equipped armies than any other state and with an aggressive spirit, was not able to break down the defenses of his enemies supported by the able strategy and tactics of Marlborough and Prince Eugene.[13] In the eighteenth century war tended to a stalemate. The professional armies tended to maneuver with relatively small casualties and with a considerable respect for the rules of war and military etiquette. Neutral rights were respected, and civilians were relatively little affected by war. Frederick the Great, by discipline and the skilful combination of artillery, cavalry, and infantry, and Napoleon, by utilizing revolutionary enthusiasm, forced marches, and strategic ability, were for a time able to make better use of the existing techniques than their enemies, to achieve mobility, and to

12. By the mid-sixteenth century "strategy had drifted back into the same state in which it is found in Italy during the age of the old Condottieri—much manoeuvring with few general actions. . . . The engineer has his revenge on the gunner, and scientific fortification developed so fast that the predominance of artillery came to an end for a time. . . . Battles became rare and sieges innumerable and tedious" (Sir Charles Oman, *A History of the Art of War in the Sixteenth Century* [New York, 1937], pp. 18 and 28).

13. Elbridge Colby, *Masters of Mobile Warfare* (Princeton: Princeton University Press, 1943), p. 62.

expand empires. Great Britain, by the utilization of sea power to blockade enemies, to hold narrow waterways, and to control the seas, was, however, able to restore the balance of power in Europe whenever threatened, and herself to build an overseas empire.[14]

The middle nineteenth century witnessed important changes in the art of war. Steam applied to land transportation raised the offensive power of Grant and Sherman in the American Civil War. Bismarck and Moltke utilized strategic railroads to win rapid wars against Denmark, Austria, and France. The mobility subsequently gained by the use of motor vehicles, tanks, and airplanes increased the power of the offensive, although for a time the use of the improved breach-loading rifle and the machine gun aided the defense. Stalemate occurred in the trenches of World War I guarded by these weapons until attrition had gnawed the morale of one side. The mobility achieved by a combination of motorized and mechanized land forces with air forces—the "blitzkrieg"—overcame defenses of all states attacked not large enough to check the advance by devastation of a large area of retreat. Only Russia and China were able to offer this "defense by depth" against Axis attack. The new mobility greatly reduced the defensive capacity of any but the greatest states in the neighborhood of a great-power aggressor.[15]

The use of steam and steel in naval warfare increased the power of the offensive both in warship encounters and in commercial war, but the result was mutual attrition rather than victory for the superior naval power. The weaker naval power could do great damage with submarines, torpedoes, and mines. Modern surface warships, more dependent upon bases than wooden sailing ships, found it more difficult to dominate all the seas.[16]

On the whole, the recent war inventions have tended to increase the power differential between great powers and lesser powers and to weaken the relative influence of sea power. Admiral Mahan's theory of the predominance of sea power was questioned in the writings of Mackinder and Haushofer, who thought that land and air power, when based on the heart of the largest land mass—the Eurasian continent—would provide the basis for world control. It cannot be said that World War II decided between Mahan and Mackinder. Rather it suggested that air power was to dominate war and that it depended

14. *Ibid.*, pp. 104–7, 143; Fuller, *op. cit.*, pp. 96 ff.; Wright, *A Study of War*, I, 295 ff.
15. Fuller, *op. cit.*, pp. 104 ff.; Wright, *A Study of War*, I, 297 ff.
16. Bernard Brodie, *Sea Power in the Machine Age* (Princeton: Princeton University Press, 1941); Wright, *A Study of War*, I, 298 ff.; II, 793 ff.

primarily on industrial potential and technological skill. Ranges became such that the heartland, rimland, or other geographical character of the states' homeland was of lesser importance. Most states recognized this by organizing the air force on a parity with the army and the navy. Finally, the use of the atomic bomb, in bringing World War II to a sudden close, suggested that an offensive was possible by long-range aircraft carrying this weapon against which there was no defense but fear of reprisal. This situation, coupled with the astonishing destructiveness of the atomic weapon, presented war as an operation approaching suicide for all belligerents.[17]

The future is susceptible of various interpretations according to the assumptions made about the sources of national and world opinion and policies.

CONSEQUENCES OF POLICIES OF SELF-DEFENSE

One may assume that national opinions flow from the tradition of the group, that among these preservation of the existence of the nation will take first place, and that the distrust of other nations will prevent reliance on anything but national power to protect this basic value. With such assumptions, governments would be expected, under the impact of the greater hazards to national existence developed by the new technology, to pursue policies of national defense with increased energy and single-mindedness. Such defense would involve the acquisition or control of bases and outposts as distant from the heart of the nation as possible in order to provide watching posts for detecting sudden attacks from possible enemies and bases as near as possible to the territory of potential enemies for preventive action or counterattack upon them. With such policies, the great powers might be expected to bring smaller neighbors within their empires or spheres of interest and to insist on controlling the foreign and military policies of such states.

Such defense would also require secure access in case of war to essential raw materials and foodstuffs. States with predominant navies might be satisfied with bases adequate to control trade routes to sources of materials short in the national domain, but states with

17. H. E. Wimperis, "Nuclear Energy in War," *Atomic Energy, Its International Implications* (London: Royal Institute of International Affairs, 1948), pp. 47 ff.; Bernard Brodie, *The Absolute Weapon* (New York, 1946), pp. 21 ff.; "The Security Problem in the Light of Atomic Energy," in *A Foreign Policy for the United States*, ed. Q. Wright (Chicago, 1947), pp. 89 ff.; Edward M. Earle, "The Influence of Air Power upon History," *Yale Review*, 1946, pp. 577 ff.; Q. Wright, "Aviation and World Politics," *Air Affairs*, I (1946), 97, 242, 383, and "World Politics and the Atom Bomb," *ibid.*, II (1947), 136 ff.

inferior navies would have an additional incentive to bring adjacent satellites with needed raw materials into their spheres.

Such defense has also been thought to require the distribution of the national population and the plants essential for military production as protection against bombing, the placing of key industries underground, the initiation and maintenance of police systems for the control of espionage and sabotage, and the disciplining of the population to act on first warning of atomic attack. Such measures of preparedness might establish legal and administrative conditions little different from a perpetual state of war, and little of civil liberty or democracy might remain. All states might become garrison states subject to military order. Furthermore, since offense is the best defense, a good share of the national income might have to be spent in maintenance of vast fleets of airplanes on the alert; outposts, radar equipment, naval and land forces adequate to protect the extended empire; and considerable land forces to occupy enemy territory and to maintain domestic order after the first enemy attack. It would be expected that, in spite of all precautions, many such attacks would get through and lay waste the cities.[18]

Another theory on this subject holds that an atomic-bomb attack would not be launched against cities or industrial plants but would be launched against airplanes, atomic-bomb stocks, and plane and rocket bases on land or on naval vessels in order to prevent retaliation. Thus, instead of attack upon the national nerve and production centers foreseen by Douhet and Seversky and practiced in World War II, attack would be confined in the first stage to the enemies' armed forces in being as it was in the eighteenth century. If one side succeeded in destroying the enemy's capacity for atomic attack before it had exhausted its own supply of weapons for this purpose, the enemy might surrender to save its cities. If both sides had exhausted atomic weapons in the first stage, traditional methods of invasion and occupation might be undertaken.

In any case, according to this school of thought, efforts to protect cities or to distribute industry would be futile and a waste of resources better spent otherwise. Preparation for defense should give first attention to an efficient intelligence service and widely distributed detection and counterattack bases under commands capable of acting immediately and without continuing central direction. On notice of enemy approach, the population might be evacuated from

18. W. F. Ogburn, *The Social Effects of Aviation* (Boston, 1946), pp. 698 ff.

cities to prearranged farms, and all industrial production might be abandoned. Victory or defeat in the first stage, which would probably be the last, would depend on the supply of air- or rocket-borne atomic weapons in being. Preparation in accord with this theory would not involve regimentation, militarization, or displacement of the civil population. Since protection of cities and industry would not be in the scheme of defense, elaborate antisabotage and domestic espionage measures would not be necessary. Civil liberties and democracy might continue until war began, though large expenditures would be necessary to maintain the numerous bases with their skilled personnel, the detection devices always on the alert, and the huge stores of atomic weapons ready for instant counterattack.[19]

Defensive preparations based on either theory would probably be interpreted in other countries as offensive preparations and would stimulate their defensive measures; thus the arms race might proceed with continually accelerating speed. Little sense of security might develop.

Under present conditions the United States and the Soviet Union have such predominance that gradually most of the remainder of the world may come under the spheres of one or the other. As the process develops, it may appear that time favors one or the other. Since both may anticipate eventual war, the one against which time is running may start a war of "necessary self-defense," if in the meanwhile its rival, feeling that it has markedly superior techniques, has not already embarked upon a "necessary preventive war."

Such a war may result in the elimination of one of the states and the establishment by the other of a world empire over what remains of the world order. An empire thus established by conquest may be faced by threats of internal revolt requiring that it be ruled by force. Its measures may be interpreted by much of the population subject to it as oppressive, and the wielding of such vast power may result in corruption and weakening at the center.

Such a process of development accords with the precedents of past civilizations. The China of Confucius, with over a hundred independent states in power-political relations, faced wars of increasing destructiveness as the *Ch'un Ch'iu* period moved into the period of warring states. The number of states in the system decreased even more rapidly as new military techniques, utilizing cavalry and the javelin, were imported from the Mongols and the Persians. In spite

19. William I. Borden, *There Will Be No Time* (New York, 1946).

of efforts at disarmament and international organization, eventually the Ch'in conquered the states that remained and established the first empire in 225 B.C. After a few centuries the Han, which succeeded the Ch'in dynasty, dissolved in civil war and external invasion, and the old civilization of China came to an end.[20]

The story was similar in the progress of the power political rivalries of the Greek city-states. After their absorption by the Macedonian Empire, utilizing the phalanx supplemented by cavalry and Alexander's genius, and the breakup of the latter into the Hellenistic states, rivalries proceeded in the Mediterranean area until eventually Rome and Carthage emerged as the survivors. After several wars Rome was victorious, with the superior military technique of the flexible legions supported by naval forces. The universal empire of the Caesars lasted for only a few centuries.[21]

Similar conditions preceded the establishment of the Egyptian Middle Empire after the Hyksos invasion had improved military technique through use of the horse; of the Persian Empire in the sixth century B.C. after Cyrus had developed a skilful and disciplined army of horse archers; of the Maurya Empire of India in the fourth century B.C. after Chandragupta had organized vast armies utilizing both the horse and the elephant; of the Mogul Empire in the sixteenth century A.D. after Babur had introduced artillery to India and employed it in combined tactics with cavalry and infantry.[22]

The progress from a relatively stable balance of power through periods of more intense rivalry, elimination of the smaller states, military invention favoring the offensive, increasing ferocity of war, bipolar power politics, universal conquest, corruption, insurrection, and decay has been the fate of most civilizations of the past. Such a development, in logic as well as in history, seems to be the expected development of policies of self-preservation by self-help as a civilization shrinks through invention in communication and transport, as the power of the offensive increases, and as war becomes more destructive through military invention.

CONSEQUENCES OF BALANCE-OF-POWER POLICIES

Another possible assumption is that preservation of the existence of the state will rank first in the opinion of each nation, but each

---

20. Wright, *A Study of War*, I, 577. The considerable development of the art of war in the Confucian period is indicated by the treatise on *The Art of War* by Sun-tzu, probably written at the beginning of the fifth century B.C. See the excellent translation with notes by Lionel Giles (London, 1910).

21. Wright, *A Study of War*, I, 581–83.   22. *Ibid.*, pp. 575–85.

nation will be prepared to support policies designed to obtain security, not through self-help alone, but through maintaining the equilibrium of the power system as a whole. Policies of certain states, notably Great Britain, have for long periods placed maintenance of the balance of power on a parity with national defense. Such policies have depended for success upon the existence of many states and a considerable number of great powers and on complex and flexible relationships of alliances, guaranties, buffer states, subordination, and superordination. Prevention of the natural trend toward simplicity and bipolarity in the power system has been a major objective if stability is to be maintained, but this has not been possible unless one state has been in such a relatively invulnerable position that it can act as balancer, throwing its weight one way or the other as maintenance of the equilibrium requires and itself renouncing any aspiration for world empire.

Such a condition, which existed in Europe during most of the eighteenth and nineteenth centuries, tends to be upset by the shrinking of the size of the system through improvements in communication and transport, by the gradual absorption of the lesser states by the greater, by the increasing vulnerability of the balancer because of military invention, by the entry into the system of outside powers unfamiliar with balance-of-power politics, and by increase in the power of the offensive through military invention.[23]

Changes of this type have impaired the stability of balances of power in the historical instances noted, although in many of these cases there was less conscious adhesion to balance-of-power policies than has been true in the modern history of Europe. Yet the latter history suggests that, under conditions of rapid change, policies of power equilibrium, while they may retard, can seldom prevent the tendency toward simplicity and bipolarity which develops from policies of national defense through military self-help. The trend toward bipolarity was evident in the development of the alliance system of Europe, beginning with the German-Austrian-Italian alliance of 1882, followed by the Franco-Russian alliance of 1892, the Anglo-French entente of 1902, and subsequent British agreements with Japan and Russia. The United States in the meantime had indicated support for the entente side in the Algeciras Conference of 1906. Bipolarity was then virtually complete, and World War I soon followed.

The hope has been expressed that independent centers of power

23. *Ibid.*, pp. 760 ff.

might be built up outside the United States and the Soviet Union.[24] The British Commonwealth, western Europe, the Near East, Latin America, China, and India might in time acquire comparable power, thus reducing the relative power position of the Big Two and making possible the restoration of a stable equilibrium. Apart from the lack of historical precedent for a continuing trend toward geographical decentralization of power without destruction of the civilization itself, it seems unlikely that such a movement would gain active support from the superpowers so long as the offensive has the advantage over the defensive, as armaments are entirely controlled by national governments, and as every possible balancer is vulnerable to attack. The United States might be glad to see western Europe revived, but not if there was an equal chance of a revived western Europe siding with the Soviet Union in subsequent difficulties. Russia might be glad to see eastern Europe revive, but only if there seemed to be no chance of a united eastern Europe throwing its weight with the United States. Once bipolarity is established, it is hard to get out of peacefully.

Perhaps such a development should not be considered impossible. If the United Nations should itself develop sufficient independent power to serve as balancer, the conditions for decentralization of power might exist. The League of Nations developed a moral and political prestige during the Locarno period which did check the trend toward bipolarity and which maintained an equilibrium among Great Britain, France, Germany, and Japan for a few years. Perhaps if the United States had joined and Russia had joined earlier, the League might have developed sufficiently to handle the Manchurian crisis of 1931. Success in that instance might have prevented subsequent aggressions in Ethiopia, Spain, Austria, Czechoslovakia, and Poland, and the power equilibrium with the League acting as balancer might have been indefinitely sustained. In fact, however, failure attended the League's efforts, and the trend toward bipolarity proceeded rapidly, leading to World War II.

The United Nations, with all the great powers participating, may succeed as a balancer where the League of Nations failed. Its task, however, is much more difficult because the conditions of the world have deteriorated. Compared with the period following World War I, there are greater economic and psychic ravages of war to repair; there are fewer great powers and shorter distances between them; there are

24. DeWitt C. Poole, "Balance of Power," *Life*, XXIII (September 22, 1947), 77 ff.

greater ideological differences and greater anxieties among both governments and people; there are greater fears of sudden attack and greater necessities of total preparedness; and there is less opportunity for statesmen to deliberate, to digest facts, to appraise alternative policies, and to guide action by reason.

If the United Nations improved its capacity to reach decisions by modifying the veto, acquired some armed forces at its own disposal, and gained substantial support of a world public opinion penetrating into all the important states, it might serve as a balancer even though its independent power was inadequate to enforce its own law. Such a position of the United Nations might reduce the intensity of the rivalry between the United States and the Soviet Union, so that other regions of the world could organize independent power, thus further stabilizing the equilibrium.

In such a situation the United States might try to occupy the role of balancer occupied by Britain during the nineteenth century. But the American constitutional system preventing rapid action, the traditional opposition of the American people to power politics, and the unfavorable conditions of the world already referred to justify little optimism in the success of such an attempt.

The greatest obstacle to restoration of a stable balance of power is the present exaggerated power of the offensive in war because of the air-borne atomic bomb and other instruments of mass destruction. The first step in stabilizing the equilibrium of power would, therefore, seem to be the effective control of these weapons. The failure of the atomic-energy negotiations has probably been the major factor in thwarting such a development, weakening the United Nations, augmenting the United States–Soviet rivalry, and accelerating the pace toward bipolarity and World War III.

CONSEQUENCES OF WORLD FEDERATION POLICIES

A third assumption is that nations may develop public opinions based not on national traditions but on allegiance to the world order as a whole. Such an allegiance would imply a merger, at least in matters concerning security, of national public opinions in a world public opinion and a willingness of nations to sacrifice a measure of national independence and sovereignty in order to create a world order able to maintain a regime of law. With such a state of opinion, governments might find it possible to join in creating a world federation.

Both experience and analysis indicate that law cannot be effectively maintained against such powerful entities as states. Law is effective in proportion as the power of the lawmaking and law-enforcing community is greater than that of its members bound by the law. Where the ratio is of the order of a million to one, as it is in most modern states, law can be effective. The use of force against law violators becomes police action and not war. Where large corporations, trade-unions, or other collective subjects of law develop great power within a state, the problem of law enforcement becomes much more difficult to solve. In the community of nations some states are so powerful that the ratio of power, even if the world community were well organized, would be of the order of three or four to one. Under such conditions enforcement of law has the character of war, as witnessed by World War II. The Axis governments were regarded by the United Nations, not as lawful belligerents, but as lawbreakers, yet the police action to bring them to justice resembled war in the material sense. Consequently, an effective regime of world law requires that the international system in which states have usually been considered the only members be changed to a federal system in which world government operates directly on individuals in respect to those matters which cannot be handled satisfactorily by any one state.

The argument that war has become intolerably destructive, that neither self-help nor a balance of power can prevent war, and that, therefore, the only salvation for either nations or civilization lies in a regime of effective world law is supported halfheartedly by many advocates of the United Nations and wholeheartedly by advocates of world federation.

The cogency of this argument has been recognized in some past civilizations headed toward universal conquest. The Greeks sought to develop the Amphyetionic League and other traditional institutions toward federation. The states of ancient China had disarmament conferences and sought voluntary agreements looking toward federation without success. Plans to save European institutions by union were elaborated by Dante, Pope Boniface VIII, and Pierre Dubois in the first decade of the fourteenth century. Similar plans have multiplied since the Grand Design of Henry IV in the early seventeenth century. Immanuel Kant thought such a development was almost certain in time through the process of trial and error, on the theory that such a federation would be more stable than any other system of politics and, when hit upon, even though accidentally, would persist. In the past, however, neither political efforts nor philosophical plans have permitted systems of power politics to move into federations through consent except in limited areas. Systems of power politics have instead moved toward empire through conquest. Voluntary federations have been achieved only by limited groups whose cultures were in considerable measure standardized and which had a common interest in defense against an outside state.

The obstacles to federation are probably little less today than they have been in past civilizations, but it may be that the motive for such federation is greater than it has ever been before because of the destructiveness of modern military techniques.

To be effective, such a partial merger of nations in a world federation must include all the important states, and such unanimity is difficult to achieve.

National public opinions require a high degree of intelligence and foresight to depart from a long tradition of independence and self-help.

Information and education is not likely to develop a world public opinion so long as it is provided by the nations themselves.

It is not easy to draft a constitution which would assure sufficient national liberty to prevent or thwart the growth of tyranny and sufficient direct world government over the diverse peoples of the world to prevent war. The difficulties in such a task increase as the situations, cultures, and institutions of the peoples bound are diverse.

Maintenance of a public opinion adequate to sustain effective government has seldom proved practical in a large state composed of culturally distinct units unless each of these units was aware of danger from an outside state. A vigorous "out" group has hitherto been necessary to maintain sufficient integration in the "in" group to preserve order when the latter has had only a slight degree of solidarity. Nations have avoided civil war by turning public attention to the danger of foreign conquest, and they have often had to endure such war when there was no external enemy to be feared. The Roman Empire, the Chinese Empire, and the United States faced internal revolt when conditions arose which made them relatively secure from external attack. Civil wars which developed in these cases were more devastating than international wars. It is worth recalling that from the Battle of Waterloo to the Battle of the Marne, the Chinese Taiping Rebellion and the American Civil War cost more lives than all the international wars of that century combined.[25] Yet China and the United States had far more standardization of culture, co-operation for common ends, and political organization than does the world today.

It is true that the need of union may be greater for the world today than it has been for any civilization of the past. Fear of atomic war and of social revolution is justified by the present conditions of technology and opinion. World federation might not prevent either of these dangers, but the effectiveness of lesser measures is even more problematical. If the sense of necessity should develop sufficiently in all sections of the world's population, the obstacles to world federation might be surmounted.

Even if an opinion favorable to this policy developed in all important nations, it would be essential to develop a process which would assure a sense of participation by all important peoples in the making of the constitution.[26] After the constitution was adopted, the process of transferring to it sufficient military power would present grave difficulties.

The United Nations Charter may be interpreted liberally, supplementary agreements may be made by the members, special amendments may be accepted, or general revisions of the Charter may succeed, and, through such measures, the United Nations may be converted into a world federation, commanding the support of all nations. The problem, however, of preserving its present relative universality in the process of making it effective to maintain its law is not easy. If one of the great powers seceded and organized its satellites against the United Nations, the trend toward war might be accelerated, and overhasty efforts to convert the United Nations into a federation might precipitate such a situation. The repudiation of the Dred Scott case and the effort to strengthen the United States implied by the election of Lincoln in 1860 with the slogan in his background, "A house divided against itself cannot stand," precipitated the American Civil War. After the Locarno agreements the League of Nations was strengthened by conclusion of the Pact of Paris in 1928, by conclusion of the London Disarmament Agreement in 1930, by successful preparation for the General Disarmament Conference, and by admission of Germany and increasing collaboration of the United States. Fear that the League might become strong enough to thwart

25. Q. Wright, "The Historic Circumstances of Enduring Peace," *Annual Report of the American Historical Association, 1942* (Washington, 1944), pp. 364–65.

26. Q. Wright, "Constitution Making as a Process," *Common Cause*, I (February, 1948), 284–86.

their ambitions may have contributed to the aggression of the Japanese military in Manchuria, the rise of Hitler, the belligerency of Mussolini, and the train of events which led to World War II. Large dissident groups, instead of submitting, may hasten their revolt against the law if the strengthening of the force behind the law, while considerable, is not overwhelming. They may become convinced that, since their opportunity to shape the world in their own design will never be better, they had better assume the risks of war at once.

At some moment in the process of establishing world federation, all important states must join in an act of faith. They must assume that the scheme will work; that, having abandoned their capacity to defend themselves with their own arms, the federation will be able to secure them their rights under the general law. Such a conviction must necessarily proceed from reason and faith rather than from experience. Such reason and faith can hardly be expected unless the forces placed behind the world government appear to be adequate.

The new technology has faced the world with serious problems. The policy of acquiescing in the natural trend according to which each important nation prepares for defense in rivalry to the others, and organizes the lesser powers in its region around it, can hardly avoid war. A policy of attempting to restore the balance of power offers little expectation of success unless accompanied by a considerable strengthening of the United Nations. A policy of developing the United Nations into an effective world federation presents great difficulties and dangers, though it appears the course of reason. Yet the rivalry of the greatest powers is such that relaxation in preparation by either of them might precipitate the war that is feared. Partial federation excluding the Soviet Union might stimulate that power to more vigorous efforts to solidify its sphere and might intensify the arms race if it did not precipitate war. A combination of caution and boldness is necessary if statesmen are to develop a world order in which freedom and democracy can exist.[27]

The human race is presented an opportunity to employ all its capacity to extricate itself from the hazardous situation into which its penetration into the secrets of nature has brought it. A world order more standardized, co-operative, and organized than has existed in the past is probably necessary to regulate the shrinking world equipped with weapons of extraordinary destructiveness and offen-

27. Q. Wright, "Accomplishments and Expectations of World Organization," *Yale Law Journal*, LV (August, 1946), 870 ff.

sive power. The balance of power moderately adequate in the nineteenth century and the system of collective security which might have been adequate after World War I are not likely to work under present conditions. If a more integrated world order were created by conquest, the scope of destruction and depth of resentments might destroy the meager bases of a world civilization which have developed. The conqueror might attempt to standardize and centralize the world without regard for cultural differences and national autonomies. Administrative and political simplification might reduce the complexities which are the protection of individual and local liberties. Enough diversity to maintain individual and group interests has been no less important to civilization than enough unity to prevent suicidal war. A world union arising from consent is more likely to provide for both than one arising from conquest. Perhaps, as in the past, greater unity will be achieved by a combination of coercion and agreement supplemented by time, during which custom and reason may gradually modify behavior. The proportion in which each of these elements enters into the process will greatly affect the adequacy and permanence of the result.

INDEX

Acheson-Lilienthal Report, 120
Africa: British expansion into, 52, 53; energy resources of, 71
Agriculture, mechanization of, 61
Air Age, military power in the, 93–97
Air superiority, importance of, in atomic warfare, 153, 157
Air war, technique of, 86–88
Airplane, international effects of the, 87, 88, 94
Algeciras Conference (1906), 191
"America First" movement, 89
American atomic monopoly, 113 ff., 119, 156–63
American Civil War, 186, 195, 196
American foreign policy, basic problem of, 107–8, 109
Anglo-French entente (1902), 191
Astec civilization, 35, 36
Astec transportational development, 31, 32
Astrolabe, 41
Atomic Age, 106–9, 145–73; defense policies in the, 113–18, 167–70
Atomic bomb: comparison to previous weapons, 149–54; and increased cost of military security, 17
Atomic-bomb inferiority, 154, 155, 167–70
Atomic-bomb monopoly, 154, 156–63
Atomic-bomb superiority, 154, 155, 163–67
Atomic disarmament, 108, 109
Atomic energy: field of isotope research in, 123; international control plan for, 120, 121, 122, 125, 149, 150; and international relations, 102–25; uranium resources for, 106, 164
Atomic Energy Act, 115
Atomic-energy control, 104, 109, 120, 121, 150
Atomic fission, 102 ff.
Atomic inventions in peace and war, 102–6, 145–73
Atomic warfare, importance of air superiority in, 153, 157
Atomic weapons, American monopoly in, 111, 156–63
Australasia, British expansion into, 55
Aviation: effect of, on international relations, 86 ff., 94; effect of, on isolationism, 89; and national unity, 91; role of, in internationalism, 98, 99, 100, 101; role of, in nationalism, 98–101; and technique of war, 86–88

Bacteriological warfare, 149
Balance of power, 75 ff., 190
Balance-of-power policies, consequences of, 190–93
Berlin Conference of 1878, 181
Britain: industrial leadership of, 59, 60; Industrial Revolution in, 2; and mass communications, 133–34; position of, in Air Age, 86, 90; power of, in nineteenth century, 1, 2, 16, 17; as sea power, 60
British Commonwealth of Nations, 79
British Empire: beginnings of, 44; expansion of, into Africa, 52, 53; expansion of, into Australasia, 55; territorial growth of, 52–56; in Western Hemisphere, 55
Brussels Pact, 110

China, economic position of, 73
Coal production, 65, 66
Coal resources, 67, 68, 69
Code Napoléon, 78
"Cold war" and mass communications, 136 ff.
Communism, rise of, 26
Compass, importance of, 41
Conference of Vienna, 181
Constant factors in international relations, 17
Control of atomic energy, 104, 109, 120, 121, 150
Crisis, international, causes of, 58, 59
Cultural standardization, contributions to, 181–85

Death rate, decrease in the, 5, 6
Decentralization, political and industrial, as atomic defense policy, 114, 115, 168, 169, 172–73
Defense policies in Atomic Age, 113–18, 167–70
Derivative effects of invention, 20, 21, 22
Diplomacy and mass communications, 141, 142
Disarmament, atomic, 108, 109
Dred Scott case, 196
Dual Monarchy, 74, 75

Economic change, political consequences of, 73
Economy: energy, 61 ff.; world, 59 ff.
Electric and gasoline transportation index, 47–48

Empires: land-borne of Horse Age, 37–40; sea-borne, 40–44

Energy economy, development of, 61 ff.; and political changes due to, 63, 64; and population increase, 62

Energy resources, 70

Europe, economic future of, 71

European Recovery Program, 110

Fascism, rise of, 26

Federation of American Scientists, 120

Fire power in war, 80

Fission, atomic, 102 ff.

Five-year plan, 4

France, colonial expansion of, 77

Franco-Prussian War, 75

Franco-Russian Alliance (1892), 191

Ganda transportational development, 31

Gas, natural, 73

German-Austrian-Italian alliance of 1882, 191

Germanic Confederation of 1815, 7

Germany: alliance with Austria and Italy, 76; colonial expansion of, 77; decrease in death rate in, 5; nineteenth-century nationalism in, 74; unification of, 75

Government in Stone Age, 33, 34

Great Britain; see Britain

Greek Empire, 40

Growth of British Empire, 44, 52–56

Growth of empires: land-borne, 37–40; sea-borne, 40–44

Growth of political area, in Steam Transportation Age, 51–53

Growth of political units, 7, 8

Hiroshima, 103, 104, 148, 151, 153, 171

Horse Age, 37–40

Horse transportation and political development, 37–40

Ideologies, relationships of, to invention, 176–80; variation in, 26

Ideology of internationalism, 97–101

Immediacy of mass communication, 126

Imperialism, 76–79

Inca civilization, 35, 36

Inca transportational development, 31, 32

India: under British rule, 5; decrease in death rate in, 6

Industrial decentralization as atomic defense policy, 114, 115, 168, 169, 172–73

Industrial development and international relations, 3

Industrial expansion, 5

Industrial leadership, 59, 60

Industrial Revolution, 2, 44; effect on naval operations, 81; influence on warfare, 79;

and population increase, 5; and world economy, 59

Industry, mechanization of, 61

Intercommunication system in the United States, 92

International control plan for atomic energy, 120, 121, 122, 125, 149, 150

International crisis, causes of, 58, 59

International relations: and atomic energy, 102–25; constant factors in, 17; effect of mechanical power on, 2, 3; human-nature factor in, 18; importance of technology in, 25; and Industrial Revolution, 58; and mass communications, 126; and relation to national security, 25; variable factors in, 18

Internationalism, 97–101; definition of, 97

Invention: acceleration in, 176; adjustment to, 16; derivative influences of, 20, 22; and destruction, 179; first effects of an, 20; and population increase, 183; reason for derivative effects of, 21; relationship of, to social ideologies, 176–80; and social demand, 177, 178; and social lag, 24, 25; war as stimulus to, 102, 103

Inventions: atomic, 102, 103; influence of peace on, 181–85; influence of war on, 185–87; in mass communications, 126 ff.

Iron Curtain, 106

Iroquois League, 34

Isolationism: and aviation, 89; in the United States, 26

Isotope research in atomic energy, 123

Italy: alliance of, with Germany, 76; nineteenth-century nationalism in, 74

Krupp process, 79

Land-borne empires: during Horse Age, 37–40; logistic growth of, 39, 40

Language groups and mass communications, 142

League of Nations, 14, 182, 192, 196

Logistic growth of empires, 39, 40

London Disarmament Agreement (1930), 196

McMahon Act, 115

Manhattan Project, 103, 104, 162

Mariner's compass, importance of, 41

Mass-communication inventions: motion picture, 128, 130; photography, 128, 129, 130; post office, 129–30, 131; printing press, 127, 130; radio, 128, 130, 131; recent and experimental, 128–29; and social institutions, 130 ff., 140, 142–43; telegraph, 127–28, 130; telephone, 127–28, 130; television, 129, 130

Mass communications: and airplane, 130;

centralized control versus unregulated ownership of, 132; and "cold war," 136 ff.; and cultural imperialism, 140–41; definition of, 126; and diplomacy, 141, 142; and Great Britain, 133–34; immediacy of, 126; as instruments of nationalism-imperialism, 133, 134, 135, 136; and international relations, 126; and language groups, 142; and propaganda, 136 ff., 141; and shooting war, 137–38; and technological changes, 126–27; and totalitarianism, 138, 139–40; and world community, 138–39

May-Johnson Bill, 116

Military power: in the Air Age, 93–97; and peacetime invention, 184; and political unity, 2; and population, 5, 6; requisites of, 2

Monroe Doctrine, 77, 93

Nagasaki, 103, 104, 151, 153, 171

National forces of cohesion, 9, 10

National optimism, causes of, 3, 4

National security, constant desire for, 25

National solidarity, factors contributing to, 9–11

Nationalism: contributing factors of, 98; nineteenth-century, 74 ff.

Natural gas, 73

Neo-isolationism, 110

New World, political expansion in, 42–44

Oil reserves, 67

Oil resources in Middle East, 73

"One World," 107

Pact of Paris (1928), 196

Pan-Germanism, 74

Pan-Slavism, 74

Peace, atomic inventions in, 102–6

Peace inventions, influence of, 181–85

Peace of Westphalia, 180, 185

Petroleum resources, 67, 73

Phoenecian Empire, 40–41, 43

Policies of balance of power, consequences of, 190–93

Policies of self-defense, consequences of, 187–90

Policies of world federation, consequences of, 193–98

Political area, growth of: and effect of steam transportation on, 47, 49; during Horse Age, 37–40

Political change due to economic developments, 63, 64

Political decentralization, as atomic defense policy, 114, 115, 168, 169

Political development: and horse transportation, 37–40; in Inca civilization, 35; among prehistoric and preliterate peoples, 29–37; and sea travel, 40–44; and transportational advancement, 29, 30, 31, 32

Political expansion: acceleration in, 32–37, 57; to New World, 42–44; of Russia, 42, 43; and relation to transportational invention, 56–57

Political growth, and steam transportation, 51–53

Political organization: adaptation of, to atomic age, 124, 168, 169; in Russia, 106, 107; at village level, 36

Political power, and peacetime invention, 184

Political units: evolution in size of, 7–12; tendency of, to enlarge, 7

Political unity, effect of, on military power, 2

Population: relation of, to military power, 5, 6; stationary, 6

Population increase, 62; and technology, 183

Power: balance of (see Balance of power); shifts of, 90–93

Power differential, increase in, 186

Powers, ranking of, 1–6; shifts in, 1–6

Pre-horse transportation and political development, 29

Production of coal, 65, 66

Propaganda and mass communications, 136 ff., 141

Rail transport as factor in world economy, 60

Ranking of powers, 1–6; relation of birth control to, 6

Ranking of states; see Ranking of powers

Resources: oil, 73; uranium, 106, 117, 164

Roman Empire, 41

Russia: air power in, 164; conflict with United States, 82, 83, 189 ff.; decrease in death rate in, 6; expansion of, 42, 43; expansion of industry in, 5, 17; five-year plan of, 4; Iron Curtain of, 106, 108; as military power in Europe, 111; and present "cold war," 112; present political organization in, 106, 107; as world power, 64

Russian-American deadlock, 109, 110, 189 ff.

Sail and steam transportation index, 45–47

Sea-borne empires, 40–44

Sea power, effect of economic change on, 82

Sea travel and political development, 40–44

Self-defense, policies of, consequences of, 187–90

Shooting war and mass communications, 137–38

Slave labor, 22

South America, energy resources of, 70, 71

Soviet-American deadlock; see Russian-American deadlock

Soviet Union; see Russia

Spanish Armada, 41

State expansion, factors affecting, 7–11
States, ranking of, 1–6
Stationary population, 6
Steam Transportation Age, political growth during, 51–53

Technological changes and mass communications, 126–27
Technological effects on society, 24
Technological influences, 20, 21, 22, 23; resistances to, 23–25
Technologies, use of, determined by social aspiration, 177, 178
Technology: in Age of Metals, 35; importance of, in international relations, 25; and population increase, 183; relationship of, to culture and public opinion, 176–80; and social lag, 24, 25; at Stone Age level, 33, 34; and warfare, 79–83; and world order, 174–98
Technology advances, acceleration in, 32–37, 49, 57
Technology of war, improvements in, 79
Thirty Years' War, 180
Totalitarianism and mass communications, 138, 139–40
Transportation, mechanization of, 61, 64
Transportation index: electric and gasoline, 47–48; sail and steam, 45–47
Treaty of Westphalia, 7

Union of European States, resistance to, 24
Union of Western Europe, 5
United Nations, 14, 182, 192, 193, 194, 196, 197; veto in, 193
United Nations Atomic Energy Commission, 120, 150
United Nations Charter, 196
United Nations Educational, Scientific, and Cultural Organization, 108
United States: and atomic-bomb inferiority, 154, 155, 167–70; as atomic-bomb monopolist, 154, 156–63; and atomic-bomb superiority, 154, 155, 163–67; conflict of, with Soviet Union, 82, 83, 189 ff.; economic future of, 71; intercommunication system in, 92; neo-isolationism in, 89; position on atomic disarmament, 108, 109; and present "cold war," 112; as world "balancer," 193; as world power, 64
Uranium resources, 106, 117, 164

Variable factors in international relations, 18
Versailles Conference, 181

War: atomic inventions in, 102–6, 145–73; and balance of offense and defense, 13; effect of technology on, 79–83; efforts toward abolishment of, 13–15; fire power in, 80; and increase in nationalism, 98; increasing destructiveness of, 12–15, 176, 179; influence of Industrial Revolution on, 79; new techniques of, 144–73; as stimulus to invention, 102, 103; as variable factor in international relations, 26
War inventions: influence of, 185–87; and power differential, 186
War technology, improvements in, 79
Wealth and aggression, 3, 4
World community and mass communications, 138–39
World economy: adjustment after World War I, 72; balance of power in, 75 ff.; of continents, 64–71; future of, 64; and Industrial Revolution, 59; rail transport as factor in, 60
World federation policies, consequences of, 193–98
World order: modern, development of, 180–81; modern technology and, 174–98; nature of, 174–76; variable aspects of, 174, 175
World power, United States as a, 64
World state, 11
World War III, 193

DATE DUE	
FEB 14 1996	

GAYLORD   PRINTED IN U.S.A.